TITRATIONS IN
NONAQUEOUS SOLVENTS

TITRATIONS IN NONAQUEOUS SOLVENTS

WALTER HUBER

LUDWIGSHAFEN A/RHEIN
GERMANY

Translated by Express Translation Service, London, England

ACADEMIC PRESS   *New York and London*   1967

FIRST PUBLISHED IN THE GERMAN LANGUAGE UNDER THE
TITLE "TITRATIONEN IN NICHTWÄSSRIGEN LÖSUNGSMITTELN"
AS VOLUME 1 IN THE SERIES "METHODEN DER ANALYSE IN
DER CHEMIE," EDITED BY FRIEDRICHT HECHT, RUDOLF KAISER,
AND HEINRICH KRIEGSMANN; COPYRIGHTED IN 1964 BY AKADEMISCHE
VERLAGSGESELLSCHAFT, FRANKFURT AM MAIN, GERMANY.

ACADEMIC PRESS INC.
111 Fifth Avenue, New York, New York 10003

United Kingdom Edition published by
ACADEMIC PRESS INC. (LONDON) LTD.
Berkeley Square House, London W.1

LIBRARY OF CONGRESS CATALOG CARD NUMBER: 67-23161

PRINTED IN THE UNITED STATES OF AMERICA

To My Wife

PREFACE

Publications dealing with titrations in nonaqueous solvents are appearing in increasing numbers, and the importance of such titrations, particularly in organic analysis, is increasing at a similar rate. This development has been aided by the rapid progress made in the past decade in the field of automatic titration instruments, particularly those recording the potential curve. Recording instruments are also available for conductometric titrations. These instruments greatly facilitate routine analyses so that even those involving complicated methods can be carried out with relative ease by trained personnel.

Why should one wish to replace water by organic solvents, most of which are relatively expensive? From the historical point of view, the reason would be that most compounds are insoluble in water. Saponification with alcoholic alkalies has long been common in organic chemistry, particularly in the analysis of fats. Such methods do not merit special consideration since they have basically nothing new to offer, but are simply extensions of already familiar processes.

A much more important reason for not using water as the titration solvent is its amphoteric behavior. Thus, only a very limited range of acid and base strengths is possible in water. The strongest possible acid is the hydronium ion H_3O^+, which, in the presence of excess water, is not sufficiently acidic to give a sharp end point against weak organic bases such as aniline. On the other hand, the strongest possible base, i.e., the hydroxyl ion OH^-, is not strong enough for the accurate determination of a weak organic acid such as phenol. These limitations at both ends of the scale are so serious that many classes of substances cannot be determined by titration in aqueous solution, whereas their determination by titration in organic solvents presents no difficulty.

vii

A third and very important reason for the use of special solvents is that it is often desirable not only to determine the total quantity of acids or bases present, but also to distinguish between acids or bases of different strengths. The amphoteric properties of water would not necessarily interfere with these determinations, but the high polarity of water could. An example of this would be the titration of the two carboxyl groups of succinic acid in the presence of one another: these groups cannot be determined separately in water, but they can be easily distinguished in many organic solvents.

A fourth reason for not using water has recently become increasingly important. This relates to the analysis of compounds, such as acyl chlorides and acid anhydrides, that react with water. These substances normally are contaminated with free acids, which can be selectively determined in some cases by direct titration. It is obvious, however, that even small quantities of water in the solvent will lead to incorrect values.

It can be seen from the examples quoted that the major use of nonaqueous titrations is for the analysis of organic acids and bases. Applications involving inorganic compounds are confined to a few special cases. Still less common are determinations based on redox titrations in nonaqueous media. This is due to some degree to the fact that almost all organic solvents are attacked by oxidizing agents. On the other hand, there is no fundamental objection to the use of water in these reactions, except possibly where the solubility of the sample is low. An exception to this is the determination of water by the K. Fischer method, which has now become a standard method. It is for this very reason that the method has been omitted from the present work; the detailed treatment required would have carried us beyond our intended scope. Moreover, it has already been the subject of other comprehensive publications.

This monograph is primarily intended for the analytical chemist, and it is therefore assumed that the reader is already familiar with the fundamentals of analytical techniques. Thus, the calculation of the results has been condensed into one short chapter.

The references selected are intended less as a directory of all compounds that have been determined than as a list of publications that contribute something new from the point of view of either method or theory. It would also have been pointless to give details of the countless procedures used. We have tried instead, by presenting a theoretical and practical system based on the acid and base strengths of the substances, to enable the reader to predict the applicability of any given titration method. The tedious search for any previous mention of a given compound in the literature is thus replaced in most cases by a simple check in the table of acid and base strengths (Table I) which we consider to be fairly comprehensive. The illustrations have been taken from the literature without modification, sometimes at the expense of a consistent presentation.

I am very grateful to the Directors of Badische Anilin- und Soda-Fabrik, and particularly to Dr. M. Jahrstorfer, without whose kind permission this book could never have been written. I am also grateful to Dr. E. Abrahamczik and Dr. W. Pfab for their encouragement and criticism. I was also greatly assisted in the preparation of the manuscript by the publisher.

June, 1967 W. HUBER

CONTENTS

Chapter 4   Reagents

PART II   PRACTICE

Chapter 5   Special Notes and Analytical Procedure

PART III   TABLES

PART I

Theory

Chapter 1

GENERAL PRINCIPLES

I. Theories of Acids and Bases

According to the classic ideas of electrochemistry developed by Arrhenius, an acid is a compound that gives hydrogen ions in aqueous solution, whereas a base is a compound that gives hydroxide ions. Neutralization is the combination of these two types of ions to form water which is practically undissociated. This definition is clearly not applicable a priori to analogous processes in nonaqueous systems.

The concept of neutralization was widened to some extent by the work of Franklin and others, who founded the chemistry of "waterlike" solvents. The autodissociation of these compounds, by analogy with that of water, was formulated as follows:

$$2 H_2O \leftrightarrows H_3O^+ + OH^-$$
$$2 NH_3 \leftrightarrows NH_4^+ + NH_2^-$$
$$2 ROH \leftrightarrows ROH_2^+ + RO^-$$
$$2 RCOOH \leftrightarrows RCOOH_2^+ + RCOO^-$$

The cations formed in this autoprotolysis are known as lyonium ions, while the anions are called lyate ions. Solvents that exhibit autodissociation are known as amphiprotic solvents or ampholytes (see Section II and Chapter 4, Section I).

Thus an example of neutralization in the ammono system would be:

$$NH_4Cl + NaNH_2 \leftrightarrows NaCl + 2 NH_3$$
$$NH_4^+ + NH_2^- \leftrightarrows 2 NH_3$$
$$(H_3O^+ + OH^- \leftrightarrows 2 H_2O)$$

This theory provides a formal interpretation of acid-base reactions in amphiprotic solvents, but it breaks down in the case of solvents that do not dissociate to give protons, i.e., aprotic solvents.

The decisive breakthrough, leading to a (nearly) universal approach, was finally achieved by Brönsted (1), who based his definitions of acids and bases not on the formal chemical composition of the compound or ion in question, but on the way in which it reacts. This approach soon leads to difficulties in understanding unless the underlying principle is borne in mind.

According to Brönsted, acids are substances that can give up protons, while bases are substances that can accept protons. This definition implies that all neutralizations simply involve the exchange of a proton. Thus the acid A and the base B react to form a weaker acid A^- and a weaker base B^-, with a simultaneous decrease in the free energy of the system:

$$A + B \leftrightarrows A^- + B^-$$
$$H_3O^+ + NH_3 \leftrightarrows NH_4^+ + H_2O$$

This purely dynamic approach greatly increases the number of amphoteric substances, i.e., substances that can act either as acids or as bases. For example, in the series:

$$H_3SO_4^+ \rightarrow H_2SO_4 \rightarrow HSO_4^- \rightarrow SO_4^{2-}$$

the two middle species are amphoteric, and only the species at the ends of the series are pure acids or bases. If we think only of the structure, it may at first seem incredible that sulfuric acid could ever be a base, but it must be remembered that this designation refers only to a certain mode of reaction, namely the ability to accept a proton. One advantage of this view is that there are absolutely no restrictions regarding charge. Thus acids may be cations (H_3O^+), electrically neutral molecules (CH_3COOH), or anions (HSO_4^-), and the same is true of bases.

Most neutralizations in nonaqueous solvents can be interpreted with the aid of the Brönsted theory. Occasionally, however, we are abruptly reminded that Brönsted's theory still depends in part on the substance itself. Thus Brönsted's definition of an acid is based on the existence of protons. There are reactions, however, that are undeniably analogous with typical neutralizations, but which nevertheless clearly do not involve protons. Examples of this are the reactions of boron and aluminum halides with amines and ethers. These halides behave as acids toward indicators. Amines are bases even in the sense of Brönsted's theory.

According to the theory advanced by G. N. Lewis (2), neutralizations in general involve the combination of a substance that can accept a pair of electrons with a suitable electron donor. The latter therefore plays the part of the base, while the acceptor acts as the acid. Brönsted's theory can be fitted into this scheme if the proton is regarded as an acceptor. Departure from the classic concept is now complete, since the definition does not depend on any one element, such as hydrogen. This may be regarded, to some extent, as a revival of old ideas, since, according to W. Lewis (1746), acids are substances that taste sour and turn certain dyes red, whereas bases turn these dyes blue; the distinction is again made entirely on the basis of the manner in which the substance reacts. At the same time, this approach provides a link with purely organic reactions, such as substitutions. Nevertheless, important differences still exist.

With a few exceptions, the neutralizations used in analysis can be better explained by the Brönsted theory which appears to be particularly well-adapted to this subject. The reason for this is that the acid used in these reactions is almost invariably the proton. Since the latter cannot occur in the free state, but is always combined with bases (in G. N. Lewis's sense), the neutralizations involved are always proton exchanges; i.e., they are Brönsted neutralizations." On the other hand, Lewis neutralizations (in the narrower sense) are simple additions with no dissociation to yield a chemically essential reactant.

II. Leveling and Protolysis

When acids or bases are dissolved in amphiprotic solvents, partial Brönsted neutralization (protolysis) occurs owing to the establishment of the following equilibria:

$$AH + SH \leftrightharpoons A^- + SH_2$$
$$B + SH \leftrightharpoons BH^+ + S^-$$

(SH=solvent; AH=acid; B=base)

If the equilibrium lies well to the right, i.e., if ionization is favored, we have a special situation which Hantzsch (3) referred to as leveling. In this case the original strong acid and base are largely replaced by lyonium and lyate ions, which are the strongest acids and bases that can exist in the solvent in question. The difference in strengths originally present in a mixture of strong acids or bases is eliminated, i.e., "leveled." The resulting solutions may be referred to as salt solutions.

Many examples of leveling are known in practice, the best known being that of aqueous solutions of strong mineral acids. The strengths of these acids actually differ widely, but the differences cannot be determined in water, which, being a relatively strong base, reacts almost quantitatively with the acids to form hydroxyonium ions; instead, solvents with low basicities, such as glacial acetic acid, must be used.

Another important case is that of the solutions of many amines in glacial acetic acid. Owing to the high acidity of the solvent, the amines are largely present as the acetates; i.e., they have been leveled. In the actual titration, which can be very accurate, it is the acetate ion that reacts with the acid. The situation here, however, is more complicated than in the case of water, since, owing to the low dielectric constant of the solvent, the salts are largely present as undissociated ion pairs.

Leveling restricts the usefulness of a solvent, since it prevents the detection of differences in the strengths of the components; however, the solvent can still be used for the determination of the total quantity of acid or base present. This is not the case with a second protolytic effect, and solvents in which this effect occurs cannot be used for titrations. The interference in this case is due not to a reaction between the solvent and the compound being determined, but to a reaction of the solvent with the salt formed in the neutralization. When this process occurs in water, it is known as hydrolysis. If the deprotonated form of an acid is denoted by A^- and the protonated form of a base by BH^+, the equilibria for the protolysis are:

$$A^- + SH \leftrightharpoons AH + S^-$$

and

$$BH^+ + SH \leftrightharpoons SH_2^+ + B$$

(SH=solvent)

If these equilibria are not strongly displaced to the left, a sharp end point can no longer be expected, owing to competition with the solvent. Consequently, the solvent in question cannot be used without modification. Examples of this are:

For acids:
   (i) titration of phenol and boric acid in water,
   (ii) titration of phenol and boric acid in alcohol;

For bases:
(i) titration of aromatic amines in water,
(ii) titration of aromatic amines in dimethylformamide.

Strictly speaking, therefore, a given amphiprotic solvent should be used only for acids and bases of certain strengths. Deviations from these values lead to leveling or to protolysis with the salt formed in the titration, these effects becoming more pronounced with increasing deviation. The relationships between the acidities or basicities of solvents and the substances that can be freely determined in these solvents are shown schematically in Fig. 1.

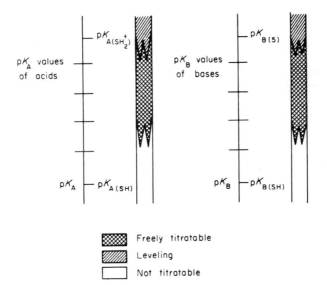

FIG. 1. Relationship between the pK values of acids and bases that can be titrated in an amphiprotic solvent SH and the pK values of the components of the solvent itself (all values measured in the solvent SH).

The smaller the dissociation constant of an amphiprotic solvent, the wider is the pK range covered by the unrestricted region. Thus basic solvents, which generally have small K values, have a particularly wide range of application. On the other hand formic acid, for example, has a much narrower range, and titrations of bases in this solvent nearly always take place in the leveling range.

Aprotic solvents are less restricted in their application from this point of view. However, they have other disadvantages, since many of them have very low polarities. Their solvent power for salts is poor and very little dissociation occurs. This can reduce the conductivity of the solution to such an extent that potentiometric determinations are no longer possible. An example of such a solvent is benzene.

III. pH Values in Nonaqueous Media

pH values in aqueous solutions are related by definition to the ionic product (autoprotolysis constant) of water, K_w, as follows*:

$$pH \equiv -\log c_{H_3O^+} = -\log K_w + \log c_{OH^-}$$

This definition can be readily adapted to "waterlike" solvents, i.e., those that, like water, are ampholytes and undergo autoprotolysis. The ionic product K_w of water is then replaced by the corresponding values for the solvents. These values are known for a number of solvents (see Part III, Table IV). If, as in the case of water, the neutrality point of the pure solvent is defined as the point at which the concentrations of lyonium and lyate ions are equal, i.e.,

$$pH_{neutral} = -\log \sqrt{K_w}$$

relationships similar to those found in water will also be found in these solvents.

Since the various solvents have different K values, their pH values at the neutrality point also differ. Similarly, the pH of a solution of an acid at a given activity does not differ by the same amount from the neutrality points of all solvents.

On the basis of this formal definition, for example, a 0.1 N solution of the very strong acid $HClO_4$ has a pH value of approximately 1, irrespective of the nature of the amphiprotic solvent used. However, this value differs by 6 units from the neutrality point of water, by 2.1 units from that of formic acid, by 8.7 units from that of ethanol, and by 10 units from that of liquid ammonia. These differences reflect the difference in the ionic products of the various solvents.

*Strictly speaking, activities should have been used instead of concentrations, but the latter are used here for simplicity.

pH Values of this nature are known as pH_p values, where the subscript p is the pH value of the pure solvent. Thus an 0.1 N solution of hydrochloric acid in water has a pH_7 value of approximately 1.

This definition of pH has the disadvantage that it can be applied only to amphiprotic solvents with relatively high polarities. A universal scale could be found if the pH were defined not in terms of lyonium ions, which occur only in amphiprotic solvents, but in terms of the hydrogen ion activity, which applies to any solvent. The following definition would then be valid for all solvents:

$$p_A = -\log a_H{}^+$$

Since the hydrogen ion activity a_{H^+} cannot be increased, this definition is of theoretical rather than practical importance.

Owing to experimental difficulties, insufficient knowledge of the material constants, etc., these two systems play only a minor role in practice. However, a third system with a more empirical basis has proved very useful. This system is based on Hammett's (4) acid function H_0. In dilute aqueous solutions this becomes the pH value, while in other solvents it assumes values derived from experimental data obtained by the measurement, in any solvent, of the dissociation of color dyes or the degree of protonation of color bases, i.e., by optical pH measurements with indicators. To find the acid function the measured degree of protonation c_B/c_{HB^+} of a color base in the solvent in question is combined with the pK value of the same base (in water):

$$H_0 \equiv -\log h_0 = pK\,(HB^+) + \log c_B/c_{HB^+}$$

Since the acid function is equivalent to the ordinary pH value in dilute aqueous solutions, this system is particularly suitable for the characterization of concentrated or nonaqueous solutions. In practice, one reference substance (indicator) is chosen, and this is compared with a second indicator having properties that can be readily altered (the indicators must be such that the required data can be satisfactorily measured for both in solutions of the same H_0 or pH value). By repetition of this procedure with more widely different indicators, it is possible to extend the scale to cover the entire range of values. The chemical relationship between the various indicators must be as close as possible, so that the ratio of their pK values will be approximately constant in all solvents (see Part III, Table III).

The H_0 values of strong acids increase much more rapidly with concentration than would be expected; for example, the value of H_0 is 100 times greater for 6 M HClO$_4$ than for 1 M HClO$_4$ (5).

In this connection, it is interesting to note that bases that are too weak to be titrated in water can be satisfactorily determined in strong salt solutions (6). Thus at high electrolyte concentrations, the water evidently behaves as if it had a low basicity.

IV. Strengths of Acids and Bases in Various Solvents

The strengths of acids and bases in aqueous solutions are found from the position of the equilibrium:

$$HA + H_2O \leftrightharpoons H_3O^+ + A^-$$

or

$$B + H_2O \leftrightharpoons BH^+ + OH^-$$

The farther the equilibrium is displaced to the right, the stronger is the acid or base in question. If we apply the law of mass action, we obtain the acidity constant

$$K_A = [H_3O^+] \, [A^-] \, / \, [HA]$$

as a measure of acid strength, and the basicity constant

$$K_B = [BH^+] \, [OH^-] \, / \, [B]$$

as a measure of base strength. Since the solutions to which these expressions apply are dilute, it may be assumed that the concentration of the water does not change and can therefore be included in the constant. Furthermore, concentrations are used instead of activities.

By analogy with the pH, the negative logarithms of these constants are known as the pK_A and the pK_B.* These are relative measures, and the

*The pK_B values of bases are sometimes replaced by the pK_A values of the corresponding neutralization products. For aqueous solutions, these values can be interconverted with the aid of the simple formula:

$$pK_B = 14 - pK_A$$

This use of the pK_A is reasonable in the interests of uniformity, but its general application in titrations can lead to confusion because the same compound can act as an acid and as a base (free form or salt form).

values are strictly valid only for aqueous solutions. For other solvents, different values must obviously be used, since the position of the equilibrium changes. A question of vital importance for titrations is whether or not the mutual relationships of acid and base strengths are the same in all solvents, since otherwise it is impossible to make any theoretical predictions.

This is in fact approximately the case for groups of chemically related substances; i.e., the pK values seem to undergo approximately equal changes in relation to the values in water (provided that no leveling occurs). The magnitude of this change depends on the position of the equilibrium. This in turn depends on the acidity or basicity of the solvent and on its dielectric properties which are approximately the same for nearly all the members of a group of chemically related substances.

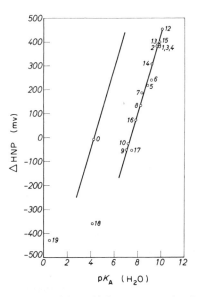

FIG. 2. Half-neutralization potentials (which are proportional to the pK values, see Chapter 1, Section V) in the potentiometric titration of phenols with tetrabutylammonium hydroxide in pyridine, plotted against the pK_A values measured in water. The deviation of substances 18 and 19 from the proportionality law is due to leveling. The parallel line on the left gives the corresponding values for carboxylic acids (see p. 17). 0, benzoic acid; 1, phenol; 2, m-cresol; 3, p-cresol; 4, o-cresol; 5, m-chlorophenol; 6, p-chlorophenol; 7, o-chlorophenol; 8, m-nitrophenol; 9, p-nitrophenol; 10, o-nitrophenol; 12, p-aminophenol; 13, o-aminophenol; 14, m-methoxyphenol; 15, p-methoxyphenol; 16, 2,4-dichlorophenol; 17, 2,4,6-trichlorophenol; 18, 2,4-dinitrophenol; 19, 2,4,6-trinitrophenol. [Streuli (7).]

A number of examples of this have been encountered in practice. Streuli (7) determined the relative acidities of a large number of phenols in pyridine, and found that they were approximately proportional to the K values in water (Fig. 2). Similar relationships have been found for the acidities of carboxylic acids in various solvents (8–10), and for the basicities of various amines in a number of solvents (11–13).

However, this proportionality almost certainly exists only for chemically related substances. Deviations from this rule, as well as the absence of proportionality between different classes of compound, can be traced to several causes and these will be dealt with in the following sections.

1. DIELECTRIC EFFECT (14)

The protolysis of an acid may correspond to one of three types, depending on whether the acid is positively charged, neutral, or negatively charged:

$$(a) \qquad NH_4^+ + H_2O \rightleftharpoons NH_3 + H_3O^+$$
$$(b) \quad CH_3COOH + H_2O \rightleftharpoons CH_3COO^- + H_3O^+$$
$$(c) \qquad HSO_4^- + H_2O \rightleftharpoons SO_4^{2-} + H_3O^+$$

A change in the dielectric properties of the solvent has a different effect in each of the three cases.

Case (a): There is no Coulomb attraction between the reacting species. The extent to which protolysis proceeds, therefore, depends mainly on the basicity of the solvent, and not on its dielectric constant (Coulomb attraction, if present, is inversely proportional to the dielectric constant).

Case (b): In this case the Coulomb attraction is such that it tends to suppress dissociation. The acidity of an acid will therefore increase with the dielectric constant of the solvent, owing to the accompanying decrease in the Coulomb attraction.

Case (c): This effect is even more pronounced where the acid already carries a negative charge, since dissociation in this case leads to an ion with a double negative charge.

It follows that the acidity constants of, for example, the positively charged ammonium ion in water and in alcohol (which have approximately equal basicities) are effectively the same. Since the two solvents differ appreciably in their dielectric constants, however, the acidity of a carboxylic acid is much lower in alcohol than in water. If a carboxylic acid and the ammonium ion have equal acidities in water, neither of the two substances can be titrated in the presence of the other; in a less polar solvent, however, the carboxylic acid will be much less acidic, and it may then be possible to titrate the two substances separately. In the case of succinic acid, titrations in water permit only the determination of the total of the two acid groups. If we use a solvent with a lower dielectric constant, on the other hand, the negatively charged acid [the acid salt obtained when the original acid is half neutralized, case *(c)*] is much less acidic than a neutral acid, so that the two acid groups can be determined separately (cf. Figs. 3, 59, and 60).

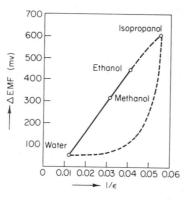

FIG. 3. Titratability of the two acid hydrogens of sulfuric acid in solvents having different dielectric constants. The difference ΔEMF between the half-neutralization potentials of the two stages is plotted against the reciprocal $1/\epsilon$ of the dielectric constant of the solvent. The finely dotted line gives corresponding values for isopropanol/water mixtures, in which ϵ (or $1/\epsilon$) does not appear to be the only factor that determines the separation of the acid stages. [Harlow and Bruss (14a).]

Special phenomena are observed in solvents with very low dielectric constants, since there is very little dissociation into ions in such media. It is well known, for example, that carboxylic acids tend to dimerize by the formation of hydrogen bonds. It has now been found from potentiometric (15, 16), conductometric (17), cryoscopic (18), and IR spectroscopic (19) studies that, during titrations in nonpolar solvents, carboxylic acids combine with their own anions to form associates which are more stable than the usual carboxylic acid dimers. The result is a two-stage dissociation giving two steps in the potential curve, and two points of inflection in the conductometric curve*:

*These ions do not in fact occur in the free form, but exist largely as ion pairs.

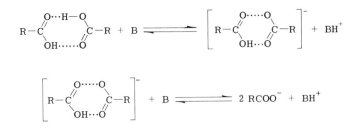

In titrations in nonpolar solvents, therefore, inflections in the potential curve before neutralization is complete must be viewed with caution, since these do not necessarily mean that the substance is not uniform. However, this abnormal behavior can be suppressed by small quantities ($\sim 1\%$) of alcohol, so that there is little danger of interference if the titrations are carried out in solvents containing alcohol.

These effects may also occur with phenols, since an extra step observed near the half-neutralization potential (16, 20) could point to the existence of the ion.

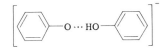

The phenols as a class are particularly useful for the study of this phenomenon, owing to the wide chemical variations that are possible within this class (16). Thus phenols with pronounced steric hindrance (*o*, *o'*-disubstituted) do not exhibit this effect, evidently because hydrogen bonding is impossible (Fig. 4). *o*-Nitrophenol, unlike *m*- and *p*-nitrophenols, also fails to show the effect, owing to intramolecular hydrogen bonding. The potential curves of thiophenols are also free from extra inflections, since sulfur, unlike oxygen, has no tendency to form hydrogen bonds.

Where the hydrogen bonding is less pronounced, so that there are no additional inflections, a steeper potential curve is obtained (see Fig. 5). This is undesirable since it is more difficult under these conditions to carry out titrations in stages. This behavior is observed in the determination of phenols in acetone (21, 22) (Fig. 5) and in pyridine (9), as well as in the titration of urea in nitromethane (23).

This brings us to a second cause of nonproportionality of the K values in different solvents, which will be described in the next section.

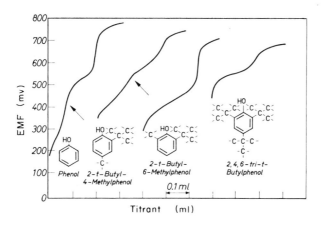

FIG. 4. Irregular potentiometric breaks in the titration of various phenols in toluene (arrows). The effect does not occur in the case of *o*-disubstituted phenols. Titrant: tetrabutylammonium hydroxide; glass and calomel electrodes. The curves are displaced horizontally for the sake of clarity. [Harlow and Bruss (16).]

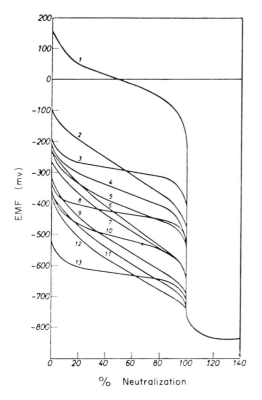

FIG. 5. Association in the titration of phenols in acetone, characterized by a steep potentiometric curve. This effect is more or less absent in the case of the *o*-substituted derivatives 1, 3, 8, 10, and 13. Titrant: 0.1 *N* triethylbutylammonium hydroxide; glass and calomel electrodes. 1, 2,4-dinitrophenol; 2, *p*-nitrophenol; 3, 2,6-dibromophenol; 4, *o*-nitrophenol; 5, salicylaldehyde; 6, *m*-nitrophenol; 7, *o*-bromophenol; 8, 1-nitroso-2-naphthol; 9, *m*-bromophenol; 10, *o*-hydroxyacetophenol; 11, 2-naphthol; 12, phenol; 13, methyl salicylate. [Fritz and Yamamura (22).]

2. SPECIFIC SOLVENT EFFECTS

The influence of the dielectric constant on the K values of acids and bases is relatively uncomplicated, and it is even possible to derive rough quantitative relationships. However, this is no longer true in the case of specific solvent effects. These may be due to familiar factors, such as hydrogen bonding with the solvent, but they may also be caused by factors that occur only in one particular case. It is therefore impossible to give even a moderately complete description of possible solvent effects, particularly since the data available are not sufficiently comprehensive, and since many of the reported values are not strictly comparable, owing to differences in the methods by which they were obtained.

A good example of the interesting but complex situations encountered is the abnormal behavior of a number of substituted benzoic acids, which was first reported by Miron and Hercules (24). While the K_A values of most of these acids exhibit satisfactory proportionality, from one solvent to another, p-aminobenzoic acid becomes much more acidic in comparison with the other acids in solvents that contain nitro groups. Miron and Hercules attributed this to the formation of a π complex with the solvent, preventing the transmission of the electron-repelling action of the amino group across the ring to decrease the acidity of the carboxyl group. Similar behavior by p-methylbenzoic acid is attributed to interruption of the hyperconjugation effect. m-Aminobenzoic acid provides an example of the dielectric effect. The relative increase in its acidity as the dielectric constant of the solvent is decreased suggests that it exists as a zwitterion (see Section IV, 1).

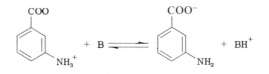

No satisfactory explanation has so far been advanced for the relative decrease in the acidity of p-nitrobenzoic acid in highly polar solvents.

Another example is found in the titration of hydroxybenzoic acids in pyridine. The *para* and *meta* isomers show two potential steps corresponding to the two acidic functions present. Salicylic acid, on the other hand, behaves as a monobasic acid (25) (Fig. 61). The proton of the phenolic group is evidently fixed by hydrogen bonding. However, both of the acidic functions in salicylic acid can be detected in ethylenediamine, which is a strongly basic, amphiprotic solvent (26).

Specific solvent influences are probably also responsible for the non-proportionality of the K values of different classes of substances in different solvents. A very good example was described by Streuli (7), who compared the acidities of phenols and carboxylic acids in pyridine and in water. A fairly strict proportionality is observed within each of these classes of substances; in pyridine, however, phenols are much more acidic than carboxylic acids. The difference between the pK_A values in water and in pyridine is 3.4 times as great for phenols as for carboxylic acids. The result is that o-nitrophenol in pyridine has roughly the same acidity as benzoic acid, whereas o-nitrophenol is a much weaker acid than benzoic acid in water. This effect is not due to leveling, since if this were so deviations from proportionality would also be observed between members of the same group. Leveling occurs only with the more strongly acidic members, such as dinitrophenol and picric acid, and can be clearly recognized in a graphical evaluation (Fig. 2).

There are undoubtedly many examples of a similar nature, but the study of these is still in its early stages. However, behavior of this type offers attractive possibilities for the simultaneous determination of different substances in the presence of one another.

3. STERIC EFFECTS

The influence of steric effects on acidities and basicities is well known. It may be due to steric inhibition of planarity. Thus o-tert-butylbenzoic acid is a much stronger acid than its *meta* and *para* isomers, since the carboxyl group cannot twist into the plane of the benzene ring. Alternatively, the steric effect may be due to hydrogen bonding between the substituent and the carboxyl group (salicylic acid, see Section IV, 2). These effects may depend on the solvent, as is shown by the fact that the K values of *ortho* isomers often exhibit deviations from proportionality. Thus in relation to other benzoic acids, the o-substituted benzoic acids are weaker in pyridine than in water (9).

4. SOLUBILITY EFFECTS

If the salt formed in a neutralization precipitates out, the sharpness of the end point is theoretically increased, since the component that is subject to protolysis is removed from the equilibrium. The result is an apparent decrease in the pK value of a substance. This effect can often be used to obtain particularly pronounced potentiometric breaks. It can be brought about by the use of nonpolar solvents and by the use of suitable titrants, e.g., potassium methoxide instead of tetrabutylammonium hydroxide. However, these methods are of very limited value, and can only be used in special cases. Experience has shown that titration errors are often caused by the strong tendency of coprecipitation effects to occur during the precipitation of salts in nonpolar media. Moreover, the precipitate interferes to some extent with the end-point detection, particularly in potentiometric and conductometric titrations, so that this fundamentally favorable effect can easily turn into a disadvantage. Finally, the precipitates are generally not very sparingly soluble, so that the potential curve depends on concentration.

V. Determination of pK Values

Potentiometry provides a very simple means of determining the pK values of medium-strength acids and bases (i.e., acids and bases that are not leveled, and whose neutralization products are not strongly protolyzed; most of the substances in which we are interested belong to this group). The pK value is equal to the pH at the point on the potential curve that corresponds to half neutralization (the half-neutralization potential). This relationship can be deduced directly from the definition of the dissociation constant, which, e.g., for an acid HA, is:

$$K_A = [H^+] [A^-] / [HA]$$

At the half-neutralization point, since $[A^-] \approx [HA]$, we have:

$$K_A = [H^+]$$

and hence:

$$pK_A = pH$$

The same is true of bases.

Fundamentally, however, potentiometry can only give relative values; i.e., it can only be used for comparisons.

Another method must therefore be used for absolute determinations which need only be carried out for a few standard substances. The conductivity method can be ruled out for weakly polar solvents, since the extrapolation of the experimental results is very unreliable, owing to the weak dissociation of the electrolyte. Kolthoff and Bruckenstein, therefore, used a spectrophotometric method for the determination of absolute values (27, 28); however, this method can only be used for compounds that have characteristic absorption maxima and act as indicators. Compounds for which the absolute values have been obtained by these methods can then be readily compared with other compounds by the more convenient potentiometric method.

A number of investigations have been carried out using a procedure in which no absolute values need be known, all the results being referred to an arbitrarily chosen substance, such as benzoic acid. This procedure is quite satisfactory for comparison purposes. It has the advantage of extreme simplicity, particularly since the introduction of the modern recording potentiometer. However, it should not be used indiscriminately in weakly polar solvents (see Section VI). It is essential, moreover, that the compounds in question should always be compared at equal molar concentrations.

In the case of polyfunctional acids and bases, the situation is complicated by buffer action. For the quantitative treatment of this effect, see ref. (29).

VI. Neutralization in Weakly Polar Solvents, Especially in Glacial Acetic Acid ($\epsilon = 6.2$)

The first successful quantitative description of neutralizations in glacial acetic acid was published by Kolthoff and Bruckenstein (27, 30, 31). The findings of these authors are of great importance to the understanding of neutralizations in weakly polar solvents.

As was pointed out in Section II, even so-called strong electrolytes, such as strong acids and bases, are only weakly dissociated in nonpolar solvents. In the case of perchloric acid, for example, we have the following equilibria:

$$HClO_4 + CH_3COOH \leftrightharpoons CH_3COOH_2^+ \cdot ClO_4^- \leftrightharpoons CH_3COOH_2^+ + ClO_4^-$$

In strongly polar solvents the intermediate zwitterion of the above equilibria is practically nonexistent, whereas in glacial acetic acid perchloric acid exists almost entirely in this form.

Thus the over-all dissociation constant

$$K_{(HClO_4)} = [CH_3COOH_2^+] \, [ClO_4^-]/([HClO_4] + [CH_3COOH_2^+ \cdot ClO_4^-])$$

is made up from the ionization constant of the perchloric acid

$$K_{I(HClO_4)} = [CH_3COOH_2^+ \cdot ClO_4^-]/[HClO_4]$$

and the dissociation constant of the zwitterion

$$K_{D(HClO_4)} = [CH_3COOH_2^+] [ClO_4^-]/[CH_3COOH_2^+ \cdot ClO_4^-]$$

A similar situation is found with bases. The equilibria in this case are:

$$B + CH_3COOH \rightleftharpoons BH^+ \cdot CH_3COO^- \rightleftharpoons BH^+ + CH_3COO^-$$

and the corresponding constants are:

$$K_{(B)} = [BH^+] [CH_3COO^-]/[B] + [BH^+ \cdot CH_3COO^-]$$
$$K_{I(B)} = [BH^+ \cdot CH_3COO^-]/[B]$$
$$K_{D(B)} = [BH^+] [CH_3COO^-]/[BH^+ \cdot CH_3COO^-]$$

The mathematical relation between the various constants is given by:

$$K = K_I K_D/1 + K_I$$

For strong acids and bases, K is practically identical with K_D, which, in the most favorable case, has a value of the order of 10^{-5} (see Part III, Table V).

For weak acids and bases, on the other hand:

$$K \approx K_I K_D$$

It is clear, therefore, that the sequence of base strengths under these conditions may differ appreciably from that in water. Bases that exist in glacial acetic acid largely in the form of (undissociated) acetates, and which must therefore be regarded as strong bases, are leveled in the Brönsted sense. If dissociation were complete, as is the case in water, it would be impossible to distinguish between these bases by means of their base strengths. The difference that actually does exist is fundamentally due to the differences in the dissociation constants K_D of the acetates, i.e., in their tendencies to dissociate. The greater this tendency, the stronger is the base. In aqueous solutions, on the other hand, the base strength increases as the dissociation constant of the protonated base decreases. It is not surprising, therefore, that the order of base strengths may be quite different from that in water, and is actually reversed in some cases. In glacial acetic acid, for example, pyridinium acetate is a stronger base than ammonium acetate or even sodium acetate (see Part III, Table V). However, this is true only of strong bases, which are present almost entirely as the acetates, since the magnitude of K_B in this case is determined by the dissociation constant $K_{D(B)}$. If in the case of very weak bases the ionization constant $K_{I(B)}$ becomes predominant, the situation simultaneously becomes similar to that prevailing in water. The true strength of a base is therefore better characterized by $K_{I(B)}$ than by $K_{(B)}$ itself.

The picture is further complicated by the fact that, in addition to the acetates of the bases, the perchlorates resulting from the neutralization are also incompletely dissociated, and again differ from one another in their degrees of dissociation. An important consequence of this is that, in these circumstances, K_B cannot be calculated from the hydrogen ion concentration at the half-neutralization point as it can in water. (For further discussion see ref. (32); cf. also Section V). The strengths of the various bases can only be compared, and even the results of these comparisons are not quite correct. It is essential that the molar concentrations of the bases should be the same.

Empirical conclusions of a similar nature were reached by van der Heijde and Dahmen from the half-neutralization potentials of various weak acids in pyridine (33).

The course of the potential curve during the titration of strong bases is exactly the same as that in water. Thus the pH changes by one unit when the concentration of the base changes by a factor of ten. On the other hand, a dilution effect which does not occur in water is also observed. In a first approximation, the pH of an aqueous buffer solution (e.g., a mixture of a base and its perchlorate) is independent of dilution. In glacial acetic acid, on the contrary, the hydrogen ion concentration increases with the square root of the dilution. However, this is true only for buffer mixtures of the above type, the pH in the case of a pure salt being independent of concentration. This is of great practical importance, since the end point of a titration corresponds to the presence of a pure salt, so that the pH value at which the end point occurs is independent of concentration.

Chapter 2

METHODS OF END-POINT
DETECTION

I. Potentiometric Method

1. GENERAL

In potentiometric titrations, the electromotive force (EMF) of a galvanic cell is followed as a function of the quantity of titrant added. One half of the cell consists of an indicator electrode, which dips into the solution being titrated, and which reacts to changes in the concentrations of the compound to be determined and of the titrant. The other half of the cell is a reference electrode, the potential of which must be reproducible and must remain constant at least throughout the titration. For this reason, reference electrodes are usually electrodes of the second kind, i.e., electrodes that dip into a solution of constant composition, which is connected to the actual reaction solution via a salt bridge.

The changes in the EMF of such a cell obey the laws that apply to Nernst concentration cells; i.e., they are proportional, not to the absolute concentrations of the ions in question, but to the relative changes in these concentrations. When the concentration changes by a factor of ten the EMF changes by approximately 58 mv at room temperature.

This property enables us to find the end point, since it is at this point that the rate of change of the EMF is greatest; i.e., the end point corresponds to the point of inflection of the potential curve (34).*

The shape of a potential curve varies according to whether a strong, weak, or very weak base is titrated with a strong acid (only strong acids are generally used in titrations) and vice versa (Fig. 6; cf. Fig. 37).

---

*It is assumed that the reaction in question is symmetrical, as is the case in neutralizations. (Symmetrical reactions are those in which the coefficients on the left-hand side of the reaction equation are equal to those on the right.)

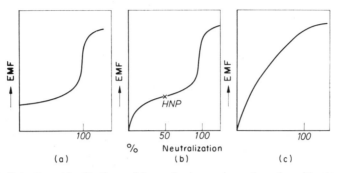

FIG. 6. Potentiometric titrations of bases having various strengths with strong acids (or vice versa): (a) strong base; (b) weak base; (c) very weak base. End-point determination impossible. The point HNP on the curve of (b) corresponds to the half-neutralization potential, and gives the pK value of the base (see Chapter 1, Section V).

The inflection of the potential curve for the titration of a strong acid with a strong base [see Fig. 6(a)] coincides with the neutrality point of the solvent, and so corresponds exactly to the end point.

The titration of a weak acid with a strong base gives a curve with two inflections [see Fig. 6(b)]. The first of these corresponds to the point at which the acid is half neutralized. The dissociation constant of the acid can be calculated from the position of this point (see Chapter 1, Section V).

The second inflection corresponds to the end point. It should be noted, however, that, owing to protolytic reactions between the solvent and the salt formed in the neutralization, this inflection does not coincide with the neutrality point of the solvent. This gives rise to a slight difference between the inflection and the true end point, so that the result is not quite accurate. However, the error involved is generally negligible. It increases with decreasing K_A of the acid and with decreasing concentration. In precision work the error should be eliminated either by calculation (when K_A is known) (35) or by standardization of the base against an acid with the same K_A value, the quantity of acid used being roughly the same as that used in the actual titration.

Very weak acids cannot be determined by this method, owing to the absence of any inflection in the potential curve [Fig. 6(c); cf. also Chapter 1, Section II].

Titration to the inflection of the potential curve is the most commonly used method of potentiometric indication. The titration may also be carried out as a differential titration (see Section I, 2). However, it is a relatively laborious method, particularly where the operator lacks practice and where the potential curve cannot be plotted automatically. In pH titrations in aqueous solution, therefore, it is quite common to use the indicator electrode simply as an ultrasensitive color indicator, and to titrate to a pH value that is known from experience to correspond to the end point. The simplicity of this method, however, is equaled by the danger involved in its indiscriminate use in nonaqueous solvents, in which electrode potentials are much less reproducible. Determination of end points by this method appears to be fairly acceptable only for the titration of large numbers of very similar samples. However, the end-point potential must then be checked by a test titration at least at the beginning of each set of titrations. This is the principle on which many automatic titration instruments are based (see Chapter 3, Section II).

2. ACCURATE DETERMINATION OF THE END POINT

If a recording potentiometer is available, it is usually not difficult to find the inflection of the potentiometric curve. If the curve is symmetrical, as is generally the case in acid-base titrations, the inflection can be found by graphical construction (see Fig. 7).

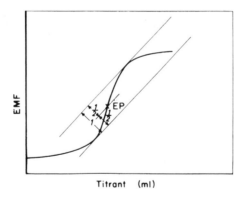

Titrant   (ml)

Fig. 7. Construction of the end point for symmetrical potentiometric curves. A line midway between two parallel tangents to the curve and parallel to the tangents meets the curve at the end point EP.

This method fails in the case of an irregular asymmetrical curve, such as may be obtained in the titration of very weak acids (phenols) owing to nonlinearity of the glass electrode in the strongly alkaline range. However, the potentiometric break itself may be quite sharp in these cases. The end point is most easily found by visual determination of the inflection. For more accurate results, the titrant solution is standardized against a qualitatively similar compound to the substance under examination.

A particularly elegant procedure is the "ring" method (36). A large number of concentric circles are drawn on a transparent film. These circles are tested against the two curvatures of the potentiometric curve to find the smallest inscribed circles that fit the curves. The line joining the centers of these circles cuts the curve at the inflection (see Fig. 8).

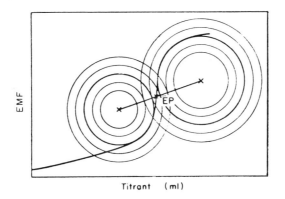

FIG. 8. "Ring method" for the construction of the end point.

Unfortunately, however, this process lacks any theoretical foundation. A similar process was described as early as 1926 (37). In this case the evolutes of the curves (i.e., the loci of the centers of all the inscribed circles) were drawn. The common tangent to the two evolutes cuts the potential curve at the end point. This procedure can also be used for asymmetrical curves, but it is rather laborious. The same is true of a mathematical procedure involving least squares (38). If no recording instrument is available, the measured potential may be plotted against the quantity of titrant added and the end point can then be found from the resulting diagram. In this case, however, it is better to plot not the potential itself, but the change in potential resulting from each addition. The curve obtained is the first derivative of the potential curve, the maximum of which corresponds to the inflection (Fig. 9).

Graphical evaluations of this type are very tedious, and are used only in exceptional cases. The end point is generally found by means of a short calculation or, more simply, by direct observation of the "break." With a little practice it is even possible to find the position of the maximum change in potential by dropwise titration in the neighborhood of the end point, particularly if the potential at the end point is approximately known. However, an error of the order of one drop must be acceptable (this is usually the case), and the break must be reasonably pronounced. Otherwise (e.g., in precision determinations and microanalyses, or where the inflection is not very pronounced), the inflection can be calculated (interpolated) from the measured potentials in the following manner (39).

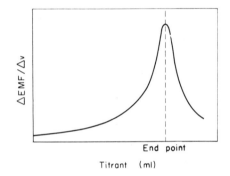

Fig. 9. Graphical determination of the end point.

As the end point is approached, the titrant is added in small and approximately identical amounts ΔV, and the change in potential is noted after each addition. If we denote these changes in potential by Δ_{max}, Δ_1, Δ_2, etc., in order of decreasing magnitude, we obtain the following picture:

volume added: 0 ΔV $2\Delta V$ $3\Delta V$ $4\Delta V$
change in potential: Δ_3 Δ_1 Δ_{max} Δ_2

The inflection, therefore, clearly lies between $2\Delta V$ and $3\Delta V$. The object of the calculation is to find the quantity $\rho\Delta V$ that must be added to $2\Delta V$ to find the position of the end point. (The above scheme covers only the small portion of the potential curve in the neighborhood of the inflection.)

To find ρ, we first compare Δ_1 and Δ_2. If these do not differ greatly in magnitude ($\Delta_1 \ll 2\Delta_2$), then

$$\rho = \frac{\Delta_2}{2\Delta_1}$$

If, on the other hand, Δ_1 is appreciably greater than Δ_2, Δ_2 will be less than $1.5\Delta_3$, and in this case:

$$\rho = 1.58 \log \frac{\Delta_2}{\Delta_3}$$

In the intermediate range, where both formulas appear to be applicable, the most accurate value is the mean of the two results.

This procedure avoids the use of Δ_{max} in the calculation; this is fortunate, since small, unavoidable errors in the volume of solution added lead to large changes in potential in this part of the curve. After each addition the potential should not be measured until a perfectly constant reading is obtained.

In another calculation method, which was described by Hahn (40), the inflection is found from the regular shape of the potential curve before the inflection is reached. However, an important requirement of this method is that the properties of the solution should remain practically unchanged throughout the titration; since this condition is not usually satisfied during titrations in nonaqueous solvents (the solvent used for the sample is not usually the same as that used for the titrant), the applicability of this method for such titrations is doubtful. It still remains to be shown to what extent methods for the mathematical "linearization" of potential curves (41–43) are valid under the conditions prevailing in nonaqueous solvents. However, these methods are too complicated for use in routine analyses.

A fundamentally different method of end-point determination involves the use of a reference electrode whose potential is equal to that of the indicator electrode at the end point. The end point can then be determined by the use of a sensitive zero-point instrument, which shows when no current is flowing in the system. The reference electrode consists of a second, identical indicator electrode dipping into a previously titrated solution, which is connected to the test solution by a salt bridge. This method is subject to the same objections as apply to titration to a predetermined potential (see Section I, 1), and, in view of the highly developed measuring instruments available nowadays, its use is probably no longer necessary.

On the other hand, differential titrations are very useful even in nonaqueous media, particularly for precision determinations. This method again involves the use of two identical indicator electrodes, one of which is screened off from the titration solution (sintered glass, perforated glass tube, etc.). After each addition of titrant, a zero-point instrument shows a deflection, since the symmetry of the cell is disturbed. The solution is thoroughly mixed until this deflection is canceled out, and the titration is then continued. The end point is indicated by a maximum in the change in potential. According to one publication (44), acids can be determined by this method with an accuracy of $\pm0.03\%$.

3. Interference in Potentiometric End-Point Detection

In this section, we shall consider only interference resulting from shortcomings in the indicating system as opposed to the electric part of the system, which will be regarded as unalterable.

There are three possibilities:

(1) The electrodes show little or no reaction to pH changes.
(2) The pH values indicated are not constant, but exhibit "drift."
(3) The pH values indicated show irregular fluctuations in both directions.

Case 1. This behavior indicates a serious fault in the electrodes. The indicator electrode may fail to indicate because of some defect, or there may be a break in the electrical circuit. Such a break would occur if the diaphragm of the reference electrode were allowed to dry out (see Chapter 3, Section V, 2).

Case 2. The electrode conditions are not constant. The most likely reason for this is sluggishness of the indicator console. In the case of a glass electrode, this means that the so-called "conditioning" of the glass electrode has been inadequate (see Chapter 3, Section V,1,a). The situation may be improved by soaking of the glass electrode, and possibly by etching of its surface (see Chapter 3, Section V,1,a).

If the indicator electrode is in order, the fault may lie with the reference electrode. Some of the components of the titration solution may have diffused into the electrode and reacted with the components of the latter. Another possibility is that diffusion of the solvent through a damaged diaphragm may cause a change in the diffusion potential, which is quite appreciable. However, these situations seldom occur to a troublesome degree.

Case 3. The most frequent trouble is irregular fluctuation during the measurement of the potential. This is particularly undesirable when the potentiometric curve is to be plotted by hand. It is less important in the case of recording instruments, since the curve is often clearly discernible in spite of the fluctuations.

This effect is observed if excessive demands are made on the instrument because the electrical resistance of the solution is too high. This may again be due to the electrodes (e.g., a glass electrode with an excessively high internal resistance, or blockage of the diaphragm of a reference electrode), or it may be a fault of the method itself. When solvents having very low polarities (dielectric constant <4) are used, the dissociation of the electrolyte, and hence the conductivity of the solution, are very low (see Part III, Table VII). The stability of the potential can be improved by reduction of the distance between the electrodes (these are already as close together as possible in the case of a single-rod measuring cell), or the conductivity may be increased in the case of a nonpolar solvent by the addition of an electrolyte (e.g., lithium chloride, see Chapter 3, Section II,2). On the electrical side, a marked improvement can be obtained by the use of a vibration capacitor amplifier (see Chapter 3, Section I). If this method is used, it is absolutely essential that the titration vessel should be screened against capacitance effects (hand capacity) by a Faraday cage (45).

II. The Conductometric Method of End-Point Detection

Conductometric titrations involve the measurement of the conductivity of the solution during the titration. The graph obtained in this way is generally linear until the end point is reached. At this point the curve turns through a more or less sharp angle, and then continues in a new direction. An important advantage of this method over potentiometric titrations is that, since the branches of the curve are linear, the discontinuity can be readily found by graphical extrapolation from a few experimental values. By suitable choice of the reacting ions, it is possible to some extent to make the discontinuity more pronounced. The reader is referred to the relevant literature (46–50) for a detailed description of the procedure.

The conductometric method is not very important for titrations in non-aqueous media, the principal reasons for this being as follows:

(1) It is much more important than in the potentiometric method to use highly polar solvents, first in order to obtain adequate conductance, and second to prevent any precipitation of sparingly soluble salts which might become attached to the electrodes. However, since solvents of this nature are mostly amphiprotic, they upset the determination in other respects.

(2) The special position of the proton with regard to the equivalent conductivity is valid only in amphiprotic solvents. Thus the changes in conductivity accompanying the disappearance or formation of protons is much less pronounced in aprotic solvents than in water.

(3) The probability of obtaining a poor conductivity curve with a blunt angle that is difficult to evaluate is a priori high, since the conductivity of the solution is generally low at first, and increases only with the addition of the strong electrolyte used as the titrant. An exception to this is found in the case of bifunctional compounds in which the two groups are titrated in succession. Compounds of this type give an N-shaped curve (51) (Fig. 10; cf. Fig. 74).

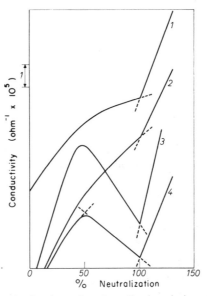

FIG. 10. Conductometric titrations of various diamines in isopropanol with perchloric acid (the curves are displaced perpendicularly with respect to one another for the sake of clarity). 1, hexamethylenediamine; 2, N,N,N',N'-tetramethylmethylenediamine; 3, N,N-dimethyltrimethylenediamine; 4, ethylenediamine. [van Meurs and Dahmen (51).]

(4) Since the shape of the conductivity curve depends not only on the pK value of the substance, but also on the transport number of the corresponding ion, the relationships prevailing are often very complex. For this reason, the method can not be used for unknown mixtures.

A special case is the conductometric determination of aluminum alkyls (52). The titration in this case is carried out in nonpolar solvents and at very low maximum conductivities. The titration curve can be recorded automatically (53).

The detection of the end point can be very difficult where there is a more or less pronounced transition region (protolysis). Grunwald (54) has described a mathematical procedure which permits the calculation of the end point from experimental values in cases of this type. In view of the laborious calculation involved, this procedure is unlikely to be considered except in special cases or in precision determinations. However, its use is essential where accuracy is required, since extrapolation of the linear branches of the curve can give rise to errors of up to several per cent. The approximation calculation of Grunwald's procedure gives an improvement of about one power of ten in the accuracy of the determination.

This should not be confused with the simple mathematical elimination of the dilution error by insertion of the correction term $V + v/V$ (where V = initial volume of solution, v = volume of titrant added). This correction is unnecessary if the original solution is sufficiently dilute and if the titrant solution is highly concentrated.

III. Voltammetric and Amperometric Methods of End-Point Detection

Potentiometry is a zero-current method, in which changes in the potential of an indicator electrode are measured against a reference electrode when almost no current is flowing. In voltammetry and amperometry, on the other hand, an appreciable flow of current between the electrodes is essential to the end-point detection. In voltammetry, one or both electrodes are polarized by a small constant current, and the changes in potential in the course of the titration are recorded. Amperometry involves the reverse procedure: a constant voltage is applied between two electrodes and the current strength is measured. Both methods require the presence of at least one redox system (sample under examination or titrant) in the titration solution. They are therefore best used in expressly redox reactions. Examples of their use for titrations in nonaqueous media are not very numerous. The so-called "dead-stop" end-point detection is often used in the determination of water by the K. Fischer method, which is one form of amperometric titration. Amperometry is also used in the argentometric determination of mercaptans. On the other hand, there are very few publications on pure acid-base titrations in nonaqueous solvents by these methods, but those that do exist show that the use of voltammetry is quite feasible and appears to be of some interest.

A detailed discussion of these two methods is beyond the scope of the present book, and the reader is referred to the original publication (55). We will, however, give a brief account of the theoretical principles of the methods. The electrode arrangement considered in both cases will be that which is most widely used, i.e., a pair of platinum electrodes (two polarizable electrodes).

In the amperometric determination of end points, consider the application of a voltage smaller than the deposition potential of the ions present in the solution. Owing to the resulting polarization of the electrodes, practically no current can flow. When the solution contains a reversible redox system, however, even extremely small voltages are sufficient to cause a finite current to flow. The processes at the two electrodes are identical, but take place in opposite directions. The shape of the current-titrant curve obtained in a titration depends on the nature of the reactants. If

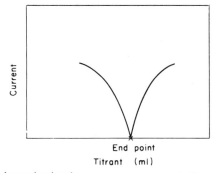

FIG. 11. End-point determination by amperometry, two indicator electrodes, two reversible systems.

the analysis consists in the titration of one reversible redox system with another [e.g., in the titration of Fe(II) with Ce(IV),* the redox systems are $Fe^{2+} \leftrightarrows Fe^{3+} + O$ (I) and $Ce^{3+} \leftrightarrows Ce^{4+} + O$ (II)], a current due to system I flows until the end point is reached. At the end point, the current falls to zero, since system I has been destroyed and system II is not yet present. Beyond the end point, a current again begins to flow, due in this case to system II. Thus the titration curve falls off to zero at the end point (Fig. 11).

*Not ideally reversible in practice.

In many cases, one of the two systems may be irreversible. One example of this is the determination of water by the K. Fischer method. In this method, only the system $I_2 + 2\ O \leftrightarrows 2\ I^-$ is reversible, so that a current flows only when excess iodine is present (iodide is always present). Thus if a standard solution of water in methanol is added to a Fischer solution, the current decreases with the free iodine content and finally reaches zero, where it remains on further titration. This is known as a dead-stop end point. If, on the other hand, water is titrated with the Fischer solution, no current flows until the end point is reached. The curves obtained in these titrations are asymmetrical (Fig. 12).

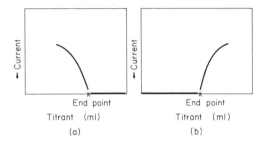

FIG. 12. Amperometric titration curves, two indicator electrodes. (a) Titration of a reversible redox system with an irreversible redox system. (b) Titration of an irreversible redox system with a reversible redox system.

The currents recorded are the same as the diffusion currents of polarography; they are therefore linearly related to the concentration of the depolarizer, provided that the electrode conditions remain constant. In the titration of very dilute solutions, it should be remembered that, as in polarography, the sensitivity of the system depends strongly on the area of the electrode surface, and to a smaller extent on the intensity of stirring.

In voltammetry a constant current is maintained between the two electrodes during the titration, and the potential difference between the electrodes is recorded. If we again consider the titration of Fe(II) and Ce(IV), the potential curve reaches a maximum at the end point. The reason for this maximum is the same as the reason for the minimum at the amperometric end point; i.e., at the end point, where the only metal ions present are Fe(III) and Ce(III), a high potential is needed in order to maintain the current.

On closer examination of the electrode reactions we find that the electrodes differ in their behavior, the potential of one electrode changing sharply just before the end point and that of the other changing just after the end point. The superposition of these two changes gives the potential maximum shown in Fig. 13.

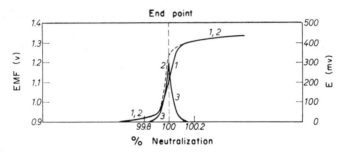

FIG. 13. Titration of 0.1 N Fe(II) with 0.1 N Ce(IV). 1, Potentiometric, platinum and calomel electrodes (left-hand ordinate). 2, Voltammetric, current 2 μa, anode potential (right-hand ordinate). 3, Voltammetric, current 2 μa, total potential (right-hand ordinate). The cathode potential (which is not shown) is the opposite of curve 2, the inflection in this case falling after the end point. Curve 3 results from the superposition of the cathode and anode potentials (55).

As in amperometry, symmetrical curves are obtained only if both redox systems are reversible. If one of the systems is irreversible, one of the electrodes undergoes only a very small change in potential during the titration. The resulting curve is similar to curve 2 in Fig. 13; i.e., it is of the same form as the curve obtained in normal potentiometry, except that the potentiometric break now occurs just before or just after the end point, depending on the reaction in question. For intermediate cases, the potential maximum will be more or less pronounced, according to the degree of reversibility of the less reversible redox system.

The difference between the position of the potentiometric break and the end point depends on the current, and is negligible at the currents normally used (of the order of 2 μa).

Since the end points in amperometry and voltammetry are indicated not by an inflection but by a more or less sharp change in a measured property, end-point detection in these cases is much easier than in potentiometric titrations. The values need not be recorded in routine work, so that a simple and relatively cheap measuring instrument can be used. Instruments that provide the constant voltage required for amperometry are commercially available (K. Fischer-titration equipment), as are the pairs of platinum electrodes. The latter can also be used for voltammetry, and a simple apparatus for the production of a constant current has been described by Büchler (56).

IV. The Use of High Frequency for End-Point Detection

In this case, changes in the resistance to alternating currents (impedance) or in the conductance of alternating currents (admittance) are recorded as a function of the quantity of reagent added. The basic difference between this and a normal conductometric titration is that the measurements in this case are carried out without electrodes. The design of the measuring cell is such that its capacitive or inductive properties can be altered during the titration. The cell is inserted into an oscillating circuit, and changes in the ohmic resistance, the dielectric constant, and, in the case of coil cells, the permeability are measured.

Since impedances and admittances are composed of reactive and active components, the measurements can be carried out by several methods. It should be noted that the sensitivities of the various methods differ with the conductivity of the solvent (Fig. 14).

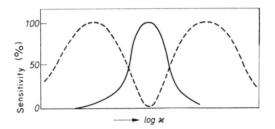

FIG. 14. Dependence of the sensitivities of various high-frequency titration methods on the specific conductivity κ. ————, reactive component method; --------, active component method. [Cruse (57).]

High-frequency methods are well-suited for titrations in nonaqueous solvents. For theoretical considerations on this process, see ref. (57).

V. Thermometric End-Point Detection

This method makes use of the enthalpy of reaction for the detection of the end point, and is therefore very widely applicable. On the other hand, the maximum accuracy that can be achieved is only of the order of $\pm 1\%$.

The method could formerly be used only for relatively concentrated solutions (about 1 N), but this limitation has been overcome by the development of very sensitive temperature-sensing elements (thermistors) and by automatic recording of the temperature curve (58). One disadvantage of this method for titrations in nonaqueous media is that it cannot be used for simultaneous determinations. Furthermore, where solvent mixtures are used, the detection of the end point may be made impossible by high heats of dilution.

The titrant solution and the reaction solution are first brought to the same temperature (the temperatures need not be absolutely identical, but the difference should always be less than about ±0.3°C). The titration is best carried out in a thermostatically controlled room, so that the two solutions can come to the same temperature. Where the temperatures of the solutions are not the same, that of the titrant solution should preferably be the lower, since the heats of the reactions are generally positive.

The titration is carried out in a Dewar flask. A very important point in automatic determinations is the response time of the temperature-sensing element which can be reduced to 1 second by the use of thermistors.

The thermometric method is particularly suitable for special determinations in which it is difficult to detect the end point by other methods.

VI. End-Point Detection by Means of Indicators

The simplest and most convenient method of end-point detection in anhydrous media, just as in aqueous media, is by means of color indicators, particularly when only occasional analyses are required. Unfortunately, the situation is not quite as simple as in aqueous solutions. In the first place, pH titrations in aqueous solvents can easily be carried out accurately to within one drop, even with 0.01 N solutions; in nonaqueous solvents, on the other hand, the end point is much more difficult to discern. The best procedure is to titrate to a certain color hue which has been found by potentiometry to correspond to the end point, but very few indicators have been studied in such dilute solutions. However, when 0.01 N solutions are used, as is generally recommended, the sharpness of the color change is quite adequate, and the only cases in which any difficulties are encountered are microdeterminations.

Second, while a wide range of indicators and the pH values at which their color changes occur are known for aqueous solutions, only a few indicators are known for most nonaqueous solvents. This is partly due to the fact that conditions vary from one solvent to another; phenolphthalein, for example, shows practically no color change in the titration of weak acids with alkalis in acetone, whereas a color change of the required intensity occurs in water and in dimethylformamide. It is not surprising, therefore, that the literature on the use of color indicators in nonaqueous solvents consists largely of collections of applications.

An exception to this is the work by Kolthoff and Bruckenstein on titrations in anhydrous acetic acid (see Chapter 1, Section VI). The point at which the color change of a color indicator C occurs is determined by the ionization constant $K_{I(C)}$ for the equilibrium with the acid HX:

$$C + HX \leftrightharpoons CH^+ \cdot X^- \leftrightharpoons CH^+ + X^-$$

which is given by:

$$K_{I(C)} = [CH^+ \cdot X^-]/[C] \, [HX]$$

The dissociation constant $K_{D(C)}$

$$K_{D(C)} = [CH^+] \, [X^-]/[CH^+ \cdot X^-]$$

is so small (max. 10^{-5}) as to be negligible, since the color after the change is that of the adduct $CH^+ \cdot X^-$ itself. The indicators used must be such weak bases that there is no appreciable acetate formation between the indicator and the acetic acid. Indicator acids have not so far been used.

Practical results of the quantitative calculations include the following (for more details, see the original publication):

(1) The sharpness of the color changes near the end point is considerably less than in comparable titrations in aqueous media.
(2) The indicator itself has a considerable influence on the sharpness of the color change. Consequently, the concentration of the indicator should be kept as low as possible (a conclusion that had previously been reached by experience).
(3) Very weak bases ($pK_B > 9$) cannot be satisfactorily titrated unless special precautions are taken (but see Section VII).
(4) In the titration of strong bases, a water content of up to 0.2% in the solvent has no appreciable effect on the color change. The titration of weak bases, on the other hand, is strongly affected, but, as was pointed out above, the determination of weak bases is not sharp in any case.

(5) Whereas the pH of the end point is independent of concentration (see Chapter 1, Section VI), the color change of an indicator is affected by the concentration of the salt. The ratio $[CH^+ \cdot X^-]/[C]$ decreases with the square root of the dilution. For a given volume of solvent, therefore, the color after the change depends on the quantity of substance used. Fortunately, however, this effect is relatively slight, and is largely eliminated by incorporation into the normality factor of the standard solution if the solution is standardized with the indicator. A slightly different normality factor is obtained by potentiometric titration (59–61), and the blank titer of the solvent (which is particularly important in microdeterminations) is also different.

VII. Photometric End-Point Detection

Photometric end-point detection (62) in nonaqueous media can be used in two cases:

(1) the substance being analyzed or the product formed in the titration is colored, or
(2) the color change of an indicator may also be measured photometrically.

Each of these two methods has its own field of application, and since case 2 is closely related to familiar methods, this will be discussed first.

The principal use of photometric end-point detection in conjunction with indicators is where the spectral difference between the two colored forms of the indicator is too small to permit optical detection.

The procedure in this case is relatively simple. The spectral transparencies of the two forms of the indicator are measured. The absorption maxima are generally so far apart that an acceptable adjustment can be obtained even with a filter photometer. The photometer is adjusted to the wavelength of one of these maxima, which should preferably coincide with a minimum or zero absorption in the spectrum of the other color. Since the measurements are generally carried out in beakers, so that the layers of sample are relatively thick, the indicator must be used at a low concentration, to ensure that the solution will be sufficiently transparent. The end point is marked by a steep increase or decrease in the extinction value. Owing to the sharp changes obtained with good indicators, graphical evaluation of the results is usually unnecessary.

The range of application of this method is, in principle, the same as for

end-point detection by means of indicators, but the reproducibility of
the results is greater, particularly in the case of dilute solutions.

A much more important application, however, is based on the fact that
Higuchi *et al.* (63–66) have found a mathematical method of "linearizing"
the extinction values obtained, so that the true end point can be determined extremely accurately by graphical evaluation. For acidimetric
titrations, the concentration ratio $[C]/[CH^+]$ of the two forms of the
indicator, which can easily be found from extinction measurements,* is
plotted against the volume of added titrant. The resulting graph is a
straight line which meets the "titrant" axis at the end point (Fig. 15).

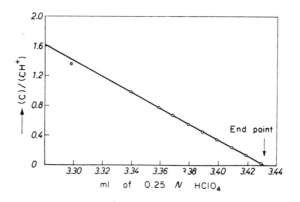

FIG. 15. Spectrophotometric titration of triphenylguanidine in glacial acetic acid with
0.25 N perchloric acid. Indicator: quinaldine red. [Higuchi *et al.* (63).]

For a given set of titration conditions, the accuracy of the end-point
detection by this method increases with the difference between the pK
of the indicator and that of the test substance. The method can no longer
be used when this difference is less than about 1.3, since the test substance and the indicator are neutralized simultaneously with the result
that the color changes gradually.

However, a method has been developed which gives good results even
under these conditions. In this case the ratio $[C]/[CH^+]$ is found from
extinction measurements and plotted against the reciprocal of the quantity
of titrant added. The resulting graph again meets the abscissa at the end
point. This method is illustrated by the titration of urea in glacial acetic

*$[C]/[CH^+] = E_C/E_{C_{max}} - E_C$ where E_C = measured extinction of C and $E_{C_{max}}$ = extinction of
C at $[CH^+] = 0$.

acid with perchloric acid, the indicator being malachite green (63). This determination cannot be carried out without calculation (Fig. 16).

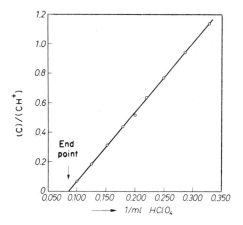

FIG. 16. Spectrophotometric titration of urea in glacial acetic acid with 0.25 N perchloric acid. Indicator: malachite green. [Higuchi *et al.* (63).]

At the same time, the slope of the line gives a measure of the basicity or acidity of the test substance in relation to the indicator. Very low basicities (e.g., that of diethyl ether) can be determined in glacial acetic acid by this method (67).

The procedure has been further modified for use with aqueous solutions and for low concentrations in glacial acetic acid, where protolysis is of some importance. The reader is referred to the original publication for this method (66).

The direct spectrophotometric determination of end points without the aid of indicators is a very special process. Many compounds, such as aromatic amines and phenols, possess indicator properties; i.e., the absorption spectra of the species obtained by protonation or deprotonation of these compounds differ appreciably from those of the compounds themselves. This property can be used to determine the content of one form of the compound or another, and hence the completness of the reaction with the titrant. The determination can be carried out by optical methods such as are used in pH measurements. However, since most of these compounds absorb in the UV region, the equipment required is generally more expensive than that used in the methods described earlier. In all but exceptional cases, in fact, a spectrophotometer will be required.

It is obviously necessary to know the absorption spectra of the reactants. However, a qualitative knowledge is quite adequate, since the extinction values are not required. This has the advantage that group determinations are possible (since related compounds often have qualitatively similar spectra).

The wavelengths used should be as long as possible, since interference can then be expected to be minimized. Thus the wavelength used for the alkalimetric titration of phenols is that of the phenoxide ion. The extinction then rises steadily to a maximum as the titration proceeds, and the determination is subject to less interference than would otherwise be the case (68) (Fig. 17).

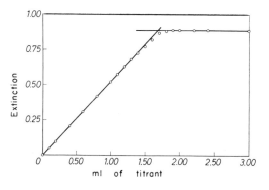

FIG. 17. Spectrophotometric titration of a phenol.

In the titration of amines, the procedure is reversed. The absorption used is that of the free amine, and the extinction falls off to a minimum as the titration proceeds (Fig. 18).

In these titrations the intersection of the two branches of the graph is taken as the end point. However, the graphs shown are idealized. The branches of the graph cannot be truly linear in practice, since the addition of the titrant gives rise to a dilution effect. To allow for this effect in the evaluation, the individual values may be linearized by means of the correction term $V + v/V$ (see Section II). In many cases, however, it is sufficient to minimize the effect by the use of dilute test solutions and relatively concentrated titrant solutions.

This is facilitated by the fact that the principal application of this method is for solutions having concentrations of the order of 0.001 M. On the one hand, other methods cannot be used in this range, and on the

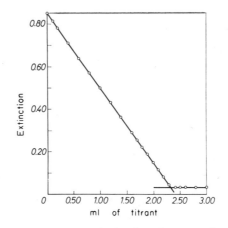

FIG. 18. Spectrophotometric titration of an aromatic amine.

other, this method cannot be used for more concentrated solutions, since the extinction values are too high to be measured accurately. The end point is more easily detected than in potentiometric titrations since it coincides not with an inflection in a curve, but with the intersection of two straight lines. In simultaneous determinations, therefore, the minimum difference in the K values for which the components can still be distinguished is of the order of 10^2 (69), corresponding to a tenfold improvement over the potentiometric method. It may be necessary in this case to change the wavelength during the titration (70).

The use of this method is subject to the following limitations:

(1) Limited choice of solvent, which must be sufficiently transparent in the spectral region to be used. [However, aromatic amines can be titrated in pyridine with an 0.001 N acetic anhydride solution (71).]
(2) The danger of optical interference by other substances increases with decreasing wavelength. It is often impossible to determine small concentrations in the presence of large numbers of other substances.
(3) The substance under investigation must be qualitatively known to some extent. The method is therefore particularly suitable for the determination of large numbers of similar components.

VIII. Precision Determination of the End Point

The maximum accuracy obtainable in titrations has been discussed in many publications, but these are mostly concerned with aqueous solutions. Owing to the many points of similarity between these and non-aqueous solutions, the accuracy that can be achieved in many cases is fundamentally the same for the two types of system. In practice, however, a number of additional factors may make it impossible to attain this accuracy in nonaqueous systems. These factors include:

(1) The coefficient of expansion of organic titrant solutions can be six times as great as that of water. Since a temperature difference of 10°C in the case of an aqueous system gives rise to a titration error of about 0.23% as a result of the thermal expansion of the glass (72), it is clear that special care must be taken to ensure that the temperature of the solutions remains constant.

(2) The titer of standard solutions is much less constant in nonaqueous systems. In addition to chemical factors, this may also be due to the higher vapor pressures of most organic solvents. Furthermore, standard solutions of alkalis are much more sensitive to contamination with atmospheric CO_2 than in aqueous media. Not only is the CO_2 more soluble in organic solvents, but the carbonates formed cause much more interference than in aqueous solutions, since carbon dioxide can be accurately titrated as such and sometimes gives the impression that a weak acid is present. This obviously applies only to the determination of acids, and bases can generally be determined without interference from carbon dioxide.

(3) Since fats dissolve readily in organic solvents, it may be difficult to seal the buret tap properly. In the case of piston burets, the piston seal may be poor because of the low surface tensions and viscosities of many organic liquids. This is particularly true in the case of glass pistons.

(4) In simultaneous determinations, it is occasionally necessary to use very weak potentiometric breaks, simply because there is no better method available. This always leads to a certain error (see Section I,1) which cannot usually be eliminated by calculation, owing to lack of information.

(5) Recording difficulties occasionally occur in potentiometric titrations in nonaqueous media. These fall into the following groups:

(a) The meter may take some time to reach a constant potential reading, since the response of the glass electrode is more sluggish in nonaqueous media than in water. This is particularly troublesome where an automatic recording meter is being used. In this case the result of the titration depends on the rate at which the titrant is added

(Fig. 19) (see also Chapter 3, Section V,1,a). Moreover the potential of the reference electrode may be inconstant because of the high diffusion potential.

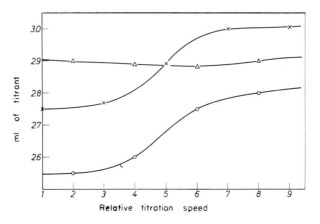

Relative titration speed

FIG. 19. Effect of the relative titration speed on the result of a titration using an automatic recording meter. Potentiometric titrations of amines in dioxane/nitroethane (4:1); titrant: 0.1 N perchloric acid in dioxane; glass and calomel electrodes. The same quantity of substance was used in every case. x, aniline (alone); o, butylamine; Δ, aniline (in the presence of butylamine). The difference between two potentiometric breaks (Δ————Δ) does not depend on the rate of titration, since the errors cancel each other out (cf. Fig. 42).

(b) The tendency of the glass electrode to exhibit nonlinearity in alkaline media is much greater in nonaqueous solvents than in water. This is particularly true of alkali metal hydroxides and alkoxides, which give poor results in the potentiometric titration of very weak acids, although the chemical reaction itself leaves nothing to be desired. Purely organic bases (tetraalkylammonium hydroxides) do not exhibit the error described above; however, in spite of the substantial improvement obtained with these bases, they are still not ideal, since the curve is often clearly distorted on the alkaline side (asymmetry) with the result that the end point is difficult to detect.

(6) Measuring vessels such as pipets are calibrated for use with aqueous solutions, and errors may arise as a result of the different surface tensions and viscosities of organic solvents.

The following precautions should therefore be taken to ensure the greatest possible accuracy:

(1) The temperature of the titrant solution should be kept constant. The error arising as a result of temperature variations can be calculated with reasonable accuracy from the coefficient of thermal expansion of the organic solvents, since these (unlike the values for water) are so large that the coefficient of cubic expansion of glass can be disregarded. As a rough guide, a difference of 1°C between the temperature at which the titrant solution is standardized and that at which the determination is carried out leads to an error of from 0.12 to 0.15%. [These figures are based on the assumption that the effect of the titrant itself ($HClO_4$, KOC_2H_5) is negligible; experience has shown that this is, in fact, the case with 0.01 N to 0.1 N aqueous titrant solutions.]

Errors due to temperature can be avoided in various ways. The best method is to work in a thermostatically controlled room. The buret itself may also be fitted with a thermostat (73). If this is not possible, the solution may be restandardized (this is the most reliable method), or the error can be eliminated mathematically.

(2) The solutions should be restandardized at frequent intervals. This is particularly important in the case of basic titrant solutions, which must also be protected from contact with atmospheric carbon dioxide. Water vapor must also be excluded from the solutions, since water generally interferes with the end point.

(3) Special care must be taken to ensure accurate measurement of the volumes delivered by the buret. Piston burets with glass pistons should not be used for accurate work; only perfectly sealed Teflon pistons are suitable. Buret taps should preferably have Teflon plugs, since there is then no need to grease the tap. Any errors due to the buret can be remedied immediately by the use of pendulum titrations* (see p. 46), but these are generally used only where extreme accuracy is required. Particularly accurate results can be obtained with a weighing buret. If the tip of the buret is to be submerged during the titration, it should be drawn as finely as possible; this is particularly important in the case of organic solvents, since the difference in density between the titrant and the reaction solution is often quite appreciable, and very rapid mixing can occur inside the tip of the buret if the titrant is the denser. Another very effective means of preventing this is to bend the finely drawn tip upwards, so that a siphoning action takes place.

*Pendulum titration = manifold back titration.

(4) In potentiometric titrations, if it is necessary to use weak potentiometric breaks, the titrant should be standardized against substances whose properties are as nearly as possible the same as those of the substance being examined. For example, in the case of a substance that gives two potentiometric breaks, the first of which is weak, a test titration should be carried out with both types of substances at similar concentrations, and with the addition of any interfering substances (e.g., water, alcohol) that may be present.

The statistical error in the end-point determination can be minimized by a pendulum titration method (74). This method is based on the repeated determination of the end point to reduce chance error. To avoid any need to carry out numerous identical titrations (for which there may not be sufficient substance available), the following procedure is used:

The sample is dissolved in a suitable solvent, and made up to a known concentration (not too low) in a graduated flask. This solution is placed in a buret, and a certain amount (not too little) is run into the titration vessel. The titrant is then introduced from a second buret. Any method of end-point detection may be used, but first consideration is generally given to color indicators. To save time, the first end point may be determined roughly, the titration being carried beyond the end point (but not too far beyond it). A small excess is then added from the first buret and preferably made up to a round figure, e.g., 20.00 ml. The next end point can now be determined quickly and accurately, since its approximate position is already known. A small quantity (e.g., 1 ml) of the substance to be analyzed is again added from the first buret, this is titrated, and the process is repeated a few more times. The titer is found by summation of the quantities used and division of one total by the other.

Example:

Volume of test solution	Volume of titrant solution
20.00 ml	A ml
21.00 ml	$A + a$ ml
22.00 ml	$A + b$ ml
63.00 ml	$3A + a + b$ ml

$$\text{titer of test solution} = \frac{3A + a + b}{63.00 \text{ ml}} \times \text{titer of titrant solution}$$

This type of calculation does not eliminate systematic errors arising from the fact that a small excess of titrant solution is required for recognition of the end point. Errors of this type are always present when indicators are used, unless the titration is carried through to a certain color hue with very dilute solutions, since it is impossible to titrate to a fraction of a drop. Fortunately, however, determinations of this nature are usually strictly reversible. These systematic errors can therefore be eliminated if the end point is approached first from one side and then from the other. The true end point is then given very accurately by the average of the two determinations. This pendulum titration, if repeated several times, also permits the elimination of the statistical error. According to reports in the literature, a skilled observer can carry out determinations by this method with an average error of only ±0.023%.

It must be emphasized that this accuracy applies only to the end-point determination, and errors due to incorrect weighings, incorrect standardization of the titrant solution (including errors due to temperature), and systematic deviations of the equivalence point from the observed end point, and errors in the calibration of the measuring vessels remain completely unaffected. However, any buret error can be recognized and even determined from a drift in the values obtained. It should also be pointed out that the above example relates to the extremely favorable case of the titration of a strong acid with a strong base.

(5) If an automatic recording potentiometer is used, any error due to sluggish response of the indicator electrode must be eliminated. In most cases the only precaution required is to carry out the titration sufficiently slowly. To be quite certain that this condition is satisfied, a number of test titrations are carried out with identical samples, but at different speeds (see Fig. 19). The maximum permissible titration speed can be seen from the values obtained. It is impossible to give numerical values here, since these depend on too many factors (state and nature of the electrode, water content of the solvents, etc.).

(6) If pipets are used to measure volumes, they should be specially calibrated. The simplest method of doing this is to use the same procedure in the standardization of the titrant solution as in the actual titration. This also automatically eliminates errors due to wetting of the buret.

(7) In potentiometric titrations, the end point is best determined by the

interpolation method described in Section I. The accuracy obtainable depends primarily on the addition of small and accurately measured quantities near the end point, and to a smaller extent on accurate measurement of the potential (75). Another very accurate method is the spectrophotometric method (see Section VII).

It is impossible to give a definite answer to the question of whether or not the introduction of automatic titration instruments increases the accuracy obtainable, since this really depends on the method. If the procedure used is very open to random fluctuations due to the "human factor," the accuracy will be improved by the use of an instrument in which the working conditions are always the same (provided, naturally, that the instrument itself works satisfactorily). However, if the end point itself is sharp, the accuracy obtainable depends mainly on the precision with which the titrant solution used can be measured. In this respect, many automatic instruments are inferior to manual operation, since they are subject to several additional sources of error.

When an automatic instrument is used, the following points should be observed in addition to the usual precautions:

In recording instruments, there may be some backlash between the chart drive and the drive of the piston buret. To minimize the effects of this backlash, the instrument is set in motion before the titration begins and the first few drops of titrant solution are rejected.

Instruments that switch themselves off automatically at the end point, which are generally used for large numbers of routine determinations, should be checked for satisfactory operation by a test titration at the beginning of each set of determinations. The main reason that this is necessary is the lack of reproducibility of the electrode potentials, since the instrument is switched off at the potential of the inflection in the curve. The potentials are particularly sensitive to water, and it is therefore important that the water content of the samples to be analyzed should be similar to that of the test substance.

Chapter 3

INSTRUMENTS

I. Potentiometers

Nearly all titrations in nonaqueous systems are carried out with the aid of the glass electrode. An efficient meter with a high resistance is therefore essential, particularly since the conductivities encountered in weakly polar solvents are much lower than in water.

Two types of instruments suitable for this purpose (known as amplifiers) are commercially available. These differ only in the manner in which electric power from the cell is amplified.

In the first type the voltage from the cell is applied to the grid of an electron tube whose current-grid voltage relationship is known. This is pure dc voltage amplification. The input resistance of such instruments can be as high as 10^{15} ohms. However, the instrument shows some null-point drift as a result of a slow change in the characteristic of the tube (aging). It must therefore be recalibrated from time to time for accuracy.

The second type of amplifier "chops" the dc voltage from the cell and gives an intermittent voltage, which is suitably amplified and then rectified again before measurement. This type has a particularly stable null point, and the instrument can set up in a very short time. On the other hand, when the chopping is mechanical, the instrument has a somewhat lower input resistance than the first type, However, in a special form of the instrument (vibrating capacitor), the chopping is due to changes in the capacity of a condenser caused by magnetically produced vibrations inside the latter (76). The input resistance of the instrument is therefore practically infinite at constant pH (in fact, it corresponds to the resistances of the insulators, which should thus be kept high), and it still remains very high when the electrode potentials change. These instruments can even be used for titrations in perfectly inert solvents, but are unfortunately rather expensive.

The scales in both types of instruments are normally calibrated in both pH units and millivolts and the sensitivity is usually adjustable. The sensitivity setting used for potentiometric titrations should be such that 1 cm on the scale corresponds to not more than 10 mv. Direct current voltage amplifiers appear to be preferable to the mechanical chopper type, in view of the higher input resistance. There are practically no restrictions on the use of the vibrating capacitor amplifier. Since the reproducibility of electrode potentials in nonaqueous media is not very good, the zero drift in tube voltmeters is not important.

Accessory instruments are sometimes offered for use with these voltmeters in titrations; these instruments compensate for the zero drift by the application of a variable voltage in the appropriate direction. In potentiometric titrations "to the break," this avoids the need for continuous subtraction of the measured readings, since the meter can be reset to zero between additions. An even greater advantage of these accessory instruments is that they permit the unrestricted use of the maximum meter sensitivity, without fear that the readings may be off scale.

II. Automatic Titration Instruments

These can be divided into two main groups each of which has its own advantages and disadvantages.

1. RECORDING INSTRUMENTS

Only a few instruments of this type are commercially available (e.g., Fig. 20), probably because of high cost, which is their main disadvantage. Their advantages are:

(1) The potential curve is recorded directly on graph paper, and can be evaluated quantitatively with respect to both the quantity of reagent consumed and the change in the potential.
(2) There are no restrictions on the choice of electrodes, since the meter has a high input resistance.
(3) The sensitivity with respect to both the reagent consumption and the potential change is medium to high.

Design Principle. The titrant is added automatically from a piston buret. The piston drive in this buret, and hence the rate of addition of the titrant, is synchronized (e.g., by means of a flexible shaft) with the chart drive, so that a given length on the diagram corresponds to a certain quantity of liquid, the exact relationship depending on the dimensions of the

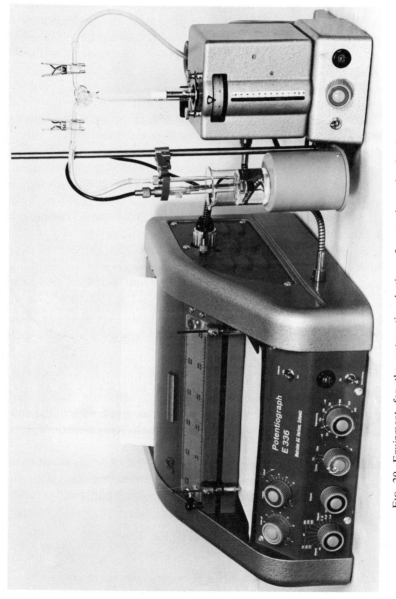

FIG. 20. Equipment for the automatic plotting of potentiometric titration curves (Metrohm AG, Herisau, Switzerland).

buret. Changes in the electrode potentials are recorded by a pen-type recorder connected to the appropriate terminals of the amplifier. The graph may be plotted either in pH units or in millivolts, and this provides another means by which the sensitivity can be controlled. The instrument can be calibrated in such a way that absolute values are obtained directly.

The titrant is usually added continuously and the speed of addition can generally be adjusted within certain limits. If the titrant is added too quickly, errors can arise because of sluggish response of the indicator electrode (Section VIII). Many instruments are therefore fitted with devices that temporarily stop the addition of titrant whenever large changes in potential occur. This gives a potential curve with steps in the region of a steep rise in the curve, but these do not interfere with the evaluation, and the reliability of the determination is increased. Instead of the potential curve, it is possible to record its first derivative. However, the value of this procedure is limited, since a satisfactory peak is obtained only when the potentiometric break is so sharp that its position can be easily distinguished even without differentiation. Nevertheless, the differential curve can be useful in the simultaneous determination of two substances that give sharp jumps situated close together. Special care should be taken to ensure that the changes in potential are as smooth as possible. Thus the conductivity of the solution should be fairly high (nonaqueous solutions are basically not very suitable for the recording of differential curves), the stirrer should be set to a reasonable speed, the electrodes used should have low resistances, and the electrode cables and mountings should be well-grounded. Even a slight irregularity in the change of potential, while having no effect on the evaluation of the potential curve, can lead to considerable difficulty in the evaluation of the differential curve.

It can be seen from the above description that instruments of the recording type are almost ideal for potentiometric titrations, since they eliminate the tedious point-by-point manual plotting of the curve. One disadvantage in comparison with manual plotting is that slow electrode processes may be overlooked (see Section VIII). However, this is partly offset by the fact that, owing to the continuous operation of the apparatus (provided that the titration speed is low and constant), weak potential jumps are more distinct than when the curve is plotted manually. The instrument permits the fast and reliable assessment of:

the usefulness of various solvents and titrants for a given purpose;
the strengths of acids and bases;
the usefulness of indicators (since the range in which the color change
takes place is shown on the potential curve).

Moreover, very satisfactory accuracy can be achieved in all potentio-metric determinations. Where large numbers of determinations are to be carried out, it is useful to have two sets of the actual titration equip-ment (piston burets and stirrers), since the refilling of the burets (particu-larly if the titrant is to be changed) is rather laborious, if not difficult.

In some of the instruments, provision is made for connection to a suit-able conductivity meter instead of to the measuring amplifier; it is then possible, with suitable electrodes, to carry out fully automatic conducto-metric titrations. In this case the (relative) conductivity is plotted against the quantity of titrant added. Although little use is made of this possibility for titrations in nonaqueous media, it nevertheless represents a valuable addition to the range of methods available.

Dead-stop titrations can also be carried out with the recording instru-ment, and combinations with spectrophotometers for the automatic plotting of the extinction have been reported (77).

2. Automatic Titrators

These are medium-priced instruments (prices between those of meas-uring amplifiers and those of recording potentiometers) designed to carry out fast determinations where many similar titrations are required. For nearly all models, the potential at the end point must be accurately known, since the instrument switches itself off at a preset potential, generally by means of a simple magnetic valve which cuts off the flow from an ordi-nary buret. To avoid overshooting the end point, the titration is carried out slowly in the neighborhood of the preset potential.

The procedure used is as follows. The substance to be analyzed is weighed into the titration vessel and dissolved in a suitable solvent. If the potential at the end point is unknown, it must first be found by means of a normal potentiometric titration; the amplifier of the automatic ti-trator can be used as an ordinary indicating meter for this purpose. Once the required potential is known, the instrument is set to this value. The buret is filled to the topmost scale marking, and the buret tap is opened fully; since the magnetic valve is still closed, no titrant flows from the buret. The instrument is then started up. The magnetic valve opens, and the potential is measured continuously, with efficient stirring. When the potential approaches the preset value, the rate of addition of the titrant is reduced to allow the indicator electrode to reach a steady potential. When the preset potential is reached, the instrument switches itself off and operates an optical or acoustical signal. The quantity of titrant used is then read off from the buret in the usual manner. A large number of samples can be analyzed rapidly with the aid of this instrument, since the titration time can be used to weigh out the next sample.

These automatic titrators are best suited to titrations in aqueous media, where potentials are reproducible and the potentiometric breaks at the end point are particularly pronounced. This second point is important in that a small error in the preset potential has little effect on the result if the break is very sharp. It should be remembered, however, that the end-point detection in this case is based on the same principle as in titrations with indicators (except that the titration is continued to a certain potential instead of to a certain pH), which give very useful results in practice; since the potentiometric method gives about a tenfold improvement in the determination of pH values, the accuracy obtainable in most cases is very satisfactory, in spite of all the uncertainties. The points discussed in Section VIII apply when these instruments are used for titrations in nonaqueous media.

There are a number of special designs which do not fit into the above scheme of automatic titration instruments. The most important of these is the Malmstadt instrument (78). This instrument, like those described above, automatically switches itself off at the end point. In this case, however, the potential at the end point need not be known, since it is determined electronically by double differentiation of the changes in potential resulting from the continuous addition of the titrant. The voltage corresponding to the second derivative of the potential curve is applied to the grid of a thyratron, and when the end point is reached the thyratron activates a relay, which closes the magnetic valve (Fig. 21). According to Maekawa (79), even better results are obtained by means of the third derivative.

One disadvantage of this apparatus is that it does not have a high input resistance, so that the glass electrode cannot be used directly. However, an amplifier may be used with the apparatus. Only relatively pronounced potentiometric breaks can be used to switch off the instrument at the end point. Moreover, since the changes in potential are really plotted as a function of time, the titration speed has a very marked influence on the reliability of switching at the end point; thus the higher the titration speed, the steeper the potential curve (as a function of time), and hence the more reliable the switch-off. Consequently, only electrodes with high response speeds should be used, and stirring must be very efficient. Nevertheless, excessively high results may still be obtained if the titrant is added too quickly. The rate of addition must therefore be carefully adjusted.

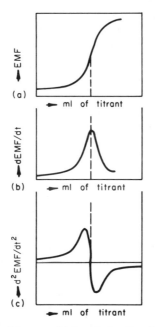

FIG. 21. (a) Normal potential curve; (b) first derivative of this curve; (c) second derivative of this curve. The dotted line indicates the position of the end point.

Malmstadt (78, 80–83) has shown that most ordinary titrations in nonaqueous media can be carried out with this apparatus and a single electrode combination (Pt[Rh]/graphite). Titrations of bases in glacial acetic acid with perchloric acid must be carried out fairly rapidly, since the potentiometric break is not very pronounced in such cases. Better results are obtained if LiCl is added to increase the conductivity of the solution. Less difficulty is encountered in the titration of acids with quaternary ammonium bases, and good results are obtained except in the case of the very weakest acids (phenols).

By the addition of an optical device, the instrument can also be used for automatic spectrophotometric end-point determinations (84, 85). In this case light of a certain wavelength is passed through the titration cell, and the intensity of the transmitted light is measured by means of photocells. The intensity changes at the end point as a result of the change in the color of an added indicator. The resulting potential curve is differentiated three times, and its third derivative is applied to the grid of a thyratron, which operates the automatic switch.

This method can be used for almost any end point that can be detected with indicators. Its accuracy is reported to be $\pm 0.2\%$.

Some of the disadvantages of Malmstadt's instrument are overcome by a related instrument (86) in which the potential curve is differentiated once. The titrant is added in portions, and the change in potential as shown by the curve of the first derivative resulting from each addition is compared with that brought about by the previous addition. At the end point, the sign of the change in potential is reversed, and the instrument switches itself off. Any electrodes can be used.

III. Burets

The burets used may, in principle, be of any conventional design. In view of the special characteristics of organic solvents, however, special attention must be paid to a number of points. The tap should be well ground in, and should turn freely. Tap grease should not be used, since it usually dissolves rapidly. Teflon taps are very useful, particularly when the titrant is an alkoxide solution. If simple burets are used, the solutions should not be left for long periods in the open buret (absorption of water and CO_2, evaporation). In the case of continuous titrations, automatic burets may be used; the air entering while the buret is being filled should be passed through soda lime (in the case of basic titrants). However, it is preferable to use syringe pump burets. The syringe pump should be connected to the titration tip by glass (ground-glass ball-joints), since rubber tubing may be attacked by organic solvents. The plunger should preferably be made of Teflon, as in most recent models, since a perfect seal is not generally obtainable with glass; however, even Teflon plungers leak if they are slightly damaged.

IV. Titration Vessels

1. With Indicators

The most suitable vessels for this purpose are Erlenmeyer flasks. However, in the case of small quantities of solution and low indicator concentrations, tall beakers may be preferable, since the thickness of the layer through which the light passes is then greater.

Where it is necessary to exclude CO_2, the titration may be carried out in an Erlenmeyer flask with a side-arm suction through which a suitably purified gas (air) is introduced. If the rate of flow of this gas is sufficiently high, the mouth of the flask need not be closed. If this arrangement is used, the liquid is agitated by means of a magnetic stirrer (it is normally easier simply to shake the flask by hand). Instead of this Erlenmeyer flask, a closed system may be used (see below). It is sufficient in many cases simply to cover the beaker with a piece of cardboard which has been pierced to accommodate the tip of the buret (87).

2. ELECTRICAL METHODS

If there is no objection to the presence of air, beakers are used. Since the minimum quantity of solution that can be used depends on the depth to which the electrodes must be immersed, tall narrow beakers should be used to avoid unnecessary dilution of the solution. Thick-walled titration beakers that taper toward their bases are particularly suitable.

If air must be excluded, the beaker may simply be covered with cardboard (see above). It is better, however, to use a completely closed system. This normally consists of a beaker with a ground-glass joint at the top. This is fitted with a ground-glass lid having several ground-glass joints (generally four). A gas inlet tube is connected to one of these joints, and two others accommodate the electrodes. The tip of the buret enters through the fourth hole, which is also the outlet for the gas.

Vessels of this type, which may also be fitted with a temperature-control jacket, are commercially available.*

The most convenient method of stirring, and that used in nearly every case, is by means of a magnetic stirrer. However, a motor-driven propeller stirrer is the most efficient means.

V. Electrodes

1. INDICATOR ELECTRODES

a. Glass Electrodes

The glass electrode has become very widely used, mainly because of its

---

*Messrs. Schott, Mainz; Messrs. Metrohm-Fuisting KG., Stuttgart-Leinfelden; Arthur H. Thomas Co., Philadelphia, Pennsylvania.

convenience. Its principal disadvantage in nonaqueous media is the poor reproducibility of its absolute potential; however, this is generally of little or no importance, since it is usual to titrate to the potentiometric break. The usefulness of this electrode is based on sharpness and linearity of indication and on fast response. The theory of the glass electrode will not be dealt with here, since it is discussed at length in the relevant literature. In the following sections we shall discuss only those aspects that are important to the use of glass electrodes in nonaqueous titrations.

α. Effect of Pretreatment. It has long been disputed whether or not glass electrodes should be soaked before being used in nonaqueous media. The difference between the two methods is as follows.

The soaked electrode gives a fast and relatively reproducible change in potential; however, it cannot be used for the absolute measurement of potentials, since it is affected by the water content of the solvent.

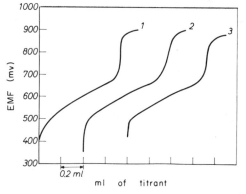

FIG. 22. Titration of phenol in pyridine with tetrabutylammonium hydroxide. 1, glass electrode, soaked for 2 hr; 2, glass electrode, dried for 2 hr with concentrated sulfuric acid, then flushed with pyridine; 3, the same electrode after being soaked for 2 hr. [Harlow (89).]

Dry glass membranes, on the other hand, exhibit almost the reverse behavior; thus while the change in potential is more or less slow [in methanol, for example, the electrode takes from 10 to 14 days to reach a constant potential (88)], the reproducibility of the absolute potential is better.

The sharpness of indication, and hence ultimately the shape of the curve, does not appear to be greatly affected by pretreatment (89) (Fig. 22).

Since the absolute potential is less important in titrations, it is theoretically preferable to use a soaked glass electrode. However, this is not absolutely essential, since good results are also obtained with dry electrodes when the time taken to reach a constant potential is long in comparison with the actual titration time. This is particularly true in the case of recording instruments in which, owing to the continuous operation, a slight potential drift has no effect on the result of the analysis.

There are two different electrode processes to be considered. The first of these is the so-called conditioning of the glass membrane, i.e., the equilibration of the membrane surface with the surrounding solution (swelling or dehydration of the glass surface). This process takes place more or less slowly. For use in aqueous systems, the electrode can be formed in advance by soaking, and the actual determination can then be carried out almost immediately. However, this is rarely possible for non-aqueous systems, since the conditions are constantly changing in this case. This is particularly true of the water content of the system; thus because of its high polarity and small molecular dimensions, water makes a particularly pronounced contribution to swelling, but the water content of the system is practically never known and it varies continually.

The second electrode process is the actual establishment of potential differences as a result of pH changes. This process takes place more or less rapidly (cf. Section VIII).

In titrations in nonaqueous media, these two processes are usually superimposed.

The pretreatment of the electrode, therefore, has little influence on sensitivity. However, the unintentional coating of the membrane surface by various types of compounds, such as surface-active agents or gel-like salt deposits derived from the substance being analyzed, has an adverse effect on the titration. This may be so severe that, in a series of titrations, it becomes necessary to clean the electrode after each determination. Poisoning of the glass electrode may cause not only a decrease in sensitivity (indicated by inexplicably weak potentiometric breaks), but also extreme sluggishness of electrode response and unexplained changes in potential. In simple cases, cleaning simply involves immersion for a short time in dilute hydrochloric acid and flushing of the electrode with water. If repetition of this procedure several times is ineffective (particularly in the case of an aged glass electrode, since aging causes a marked increase in internal resistance, which interferes with the measurement), the outermost skin of the glass may be etched off by immersion of the electrode in 10% hydrofluoric acid. This is a rather delicate operation, and the immersion time should be limited to a few seconds to avoid damage to the electrode. The sparingly soluble fluorides formed during the etching reaction are then dissolved out with 1:1 conc. hydrochloric acid : H_2O.

β. *Alkali Error.* The nonlinearity of the glass electrode in the alkaline region is referred to as the alkali error. This effect is particularly notice-able in the titration of weak acids. Since its magnitude depends on the nature of the cation, titrations of this type are generally carried out with strong organic bases (tetraalkylammonium hydroxides) which give only a small alkali error.

Harlow (89) has shown that even low concentrations of Na^+ and K^+ ions have a strong effect on the reading. If these ions are present in the solution to be analyzed, the potential is lower and the potentiometric break much less pronounced than would otherwise be the case (Fig. 23).

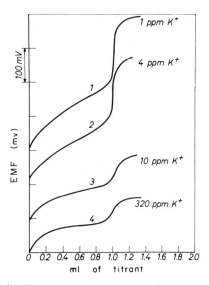

FIG. 23. The effect of various concentrations of K^+ ions on the potential of the glass electrode in the titration of phenol in pyridine with tetrabutylammonium hydroxide solution. The half-neutralization potential for curves 1 and 2 is 525 mv, while that for curves 3 and 4 is 475 mv (the curves are displaced vertically from one another). [Harlow (89).]

If, on the other hand, they are introduced with the titrant solution, they give rise to irregular potentiometric breaks. In this case, two mutually opposing electrode processes take place simultaneously; the first of these is the normal change in potential resulting from the pH change, while the second is a chemical reaction of the glass surface with the alkali metal ions, which leads to a change in the electrode characteristics (Fig. 24).

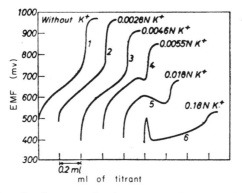

FIG. 24. The effect of various potassium ion concentrations in the titrant on the potential curve obtained with the glass electrode (titration of phenol in pyridine with 0.25 N tetra-butylammonium hydroxide). [Harlow (89).]

According to Harlow, the magnitude of the alkali error is strongly dependent on the state of swelling of the electrode. The "alkali consumption" of the electrode appears to be proportional to the thickness of the swollen layer. Even in the presence of excess alkali, however, the fall in potential is a function of the electrode that cannot be predicted; even electrodes which are theoretically identical can differ in their behavior.

b. Metal Electrodes as pH Indicators

In considering these electrodes, it is convenient to differentiate between those with defined potentials and those with undefined potentials.

α. Electrodes with Defined Potentials. The most important of these is the hydrogen electrode in the widest sense. The pure hydrogen electrode, as in aqueous systems, is of very little importance and is practically never used. A number of investigations have shown that it can be used with success in alcohol (90), acetic acid (91, 92), butyric acid (93), pyridine (94), and formic acid (95). However the reproducibility of the potential does not appear to have been absolutely established (96). The electrode material is usually platinum, but palladium is also used in some cases.

It is much more common to use modifications of the hydrogen electrode. The most important of these is the chloranil electrode, which gives an accurately reproducible potential in glacial acetic acid, and which is excellently suited for potential measurements in this solvent. It consists of a platinum electrode immersed in a glacial acetic acid solution containing the molecular compound of tetrachloroquinone (chloranil) with tetrachlorohydroquinone. The potential with respect to a normal hydrogen electrode in glacial acetic acid is +650 mv (97).

The chloranil electrode has also been used in dimethylformamide (98), dichloroacetic acid (99), and formic acid (96). It cannot be used in alkaline media, owing to decomposition of the chloranil.

The more familiar quinhydrone electrode is used for applications similar to those of the chloranil electrode. The most usual solvents in this case are alcohols, but glacial acetic acid [sometimes in the presence of acetic anhydride (100)], formic acid, ketones, and methyl glycol can also be used. To obtain better reproducibility, it is sometimes recommended that a gold electrode should be used instead of platinum (101).

β. Electrodes with Variable Potentials. The most commonly used electrode of this type is the plain platinum electrode, which can also be described as a hydrogen electrode with a variable hydrogen pressure, and which therefore has a variable absolute potential. Nevertheless, it is very useful in many cases for titration to the potentiometric break. Its great advantages are ease of manipulation and very wide applicability. It has proved particularly useful for the titration of weak and very weak acids in basic solvents such as ethylenediamine (102) and pyridine (103). However, it can also be used in the determination of weak bases in glacial acetic acid and in trifluoroacetic acid (104). Other applications include the detection of end points in liquid NH_3, the titration of hydroxyl groups with lithium hydride (105), and neutralizations in selenium oxychloride and concentrated sulfuric acid.

Malmstadt made very wide use of the platinum electrode, particularly mixed with 10% of rhodium, for his automatic titrations. Special emphasis is placed on the fact that the response is practically instantaneous, since this is a very important characteristic in these titrations.

Little use has been made of the gold electrode, but studies that have been carried out so far indicate that its properties are similar to those of the platinum electrode.

Many other indicator electrodes for pH titrations are known, but they are not used with the glass electrode. Their main advantage, namely their low internal resistance, has become practically meaningless with the development of modern measuring instruments. However, they are still used for special purposes when difficulties arise with other electrodes (e.g., alkali error in the case of the glass electrode). Electrodes that may be considered are the antimony electrode (106, 107), the tellurium electrode (106), the tungsten electrode (106), the palladium (108) or palladium hydride electrode (109), and the mercury electrode (110).

c. Electrodes for the Detection of Metal Ions: the Silver Electrode

Since reactions involving silver ions are frequently carried out even in nonaqueous solvents (determination of halogens, mercaptans, etc.), the silver electrode is quite commonly used. This electrode consists of a plain silver wire or, better, one that is coated with an appropriate silver salt. For example, for the determination of chloride, the silver electrode is anodically coated with a layer of AgCl in dilute hydrochloric acid, whereas the silver/silver sulfide electrode is used for the titration of mercaptans (111).

The silver electrode can also be used for the determination of halide ions with thallium(I) acetate (112).

In addition to its use for the detection of end points, the silver electrode can also be used to find the dissociation constants of chlorides in glacial acetic acid (113).

d. Other Electrodes

Halide ions can also be determined with mercury(II) ions. The electrode used in this case is the mercury electrode, which can be produced by amalgam formation on a gold wire (114, 115).

A special case is that of the aluminum electrode, which is used for the potentiometric titation of aluminum alkyls. This electrode must be activated by mechanical removal of the surface oxide film, followed by etching of the surface with aluminum alkyls (116).

2. REFERENCE ELECTRODES

The most commonly used type of reference electrode with a more or less well-defined potential is the calomel type. This electrode of the second kind can be connected to the solution by one of two methods. The method most commonly used in Germany, involving diaphragms of a porous material, permits the preparation of small, elegant electrodes, and there is very little diffusion in either direction. The reference electrode may also be combined with the indicator electrode (single-rod measuring cell), giving an arrangement which is very convenient to use, particularly in the titration of small volumes. This type has the disadvantage that the organic solvent can cause precipitation of the potassium chloride in the diaphragm. Interruption of the current as a result of such precipitation leads to pronounced fluctuation of the potential, or even low sensitivity of the electrode response. The electrode is therefore best stored in contact with water, which must be carefully washed off before the electrode is used again.

A second design makes use of a ground-glass diaphragm. This electrode cannot become blocked, but it permits relatively large quantities of salt solution to enter the sample, and it is also rather clumsy.

a. The Calomel Electrode

The construction of the calomel electrode will not be described here (117a). In its usual form, i.e., filled with saturated KCl solution, it is suitable for titrations in nonaqueous media, and it is in fact generally used for the sake of convenience. However, it has certain disadvantages that do not arise in aqueous media, and for this reason special constructions are used in some cases. These disadvantages include the following.

α. *Contamination of the Titration Solution by Constituents of the Salt Bridge (KCl Solution).* All the constituents of the salt bridge, i.e., K^+ ions, Cl^- ions, and water, can cause interference. K^+ ions give rise to an alkali error in the titration of weak acids with the glass electrode. Harlow (89) showed that even 10 ppm of potassium ions in the titration medium cause a distinct deterioration of the potentiometric break. If the potassium is added gradually in the course of the titration, irregular potentiometric breaks result (cf. Figs. 23 and 24).

Interference due to Cl^- ions is known even in aqueous solutions, and affects argentometric and mercurimetric titrations. This interference can be eliminated relatively easily by the use of a mercurous sulfate electrode, which contains KNO_3 solution.

A second method of making the electrode universally applicable is by means of a salt bridge, containing a solvent and a salt that have no adverse effects on the titration.

Marple and Fritz have described several salt bridges of this type (117b). The solvents used were *tert*-butanol, pyridine, acetone, and isopropanol.

Using these two- to three-stage arrangements it was possible to maintain reproducibility of the reference potential to within 2 mv for long periods (Fig. 25).

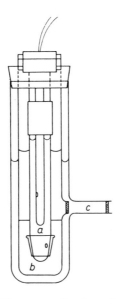

FIG. 25. A multistage salt bridge connecting the calomel electrode with the titration vessel. The electrode compartments contain: *a,* water saturated with potassium chloride; *b,* the two-phase system *tert*-butanol/water, saturated with potassium chloride; *c, tert*-butanol saturated with tetrabutylammonium bromide. Shaded areas: sintered glass. [Marple and Fritz (117b).]

Many solvents have been suggested as replacements for water in electrolyte bridges. Besides preventing the contamination of the titration medium with water, these solvents also eliminate another shortcoming of the calomel electrode, namely the following.

β. *Uncertainty Regarding the Potential.* This uncertainty is mainly due to the fact that the diffusion potential differs by several orders of magnitude from that in aqueous systems. Gutbezahl and Grunwald (118a) determined this potential between alcohol and saturated aqueous KCl solution and obtained values of 25 mv for 50% alcohol, 75 mv for 80% alcohol, and 140 mv for 100% alcohol. For accurate absolute measurements, therefore, it is essential to use a modified electrode, particularly since contamination of the salt bridge by diffusion of the solvent is unavoidable when water is used. Strictly speaking, a special reference electrode should be used for each solvent system. However, since all that is usually required in practice is to separate the water from the titration solution, it is generally possible to use electrodes in which the water in the salt bridge has been replaced by a harmless solvent. Practical experience has shown that the salt bridge should satisfy the following requirements:

(1) Inert solvent, as highly polar as possible, vapor pressure not too high (to avoid rapid drying out).
(2) Replacement of the potassium ion by the tetrabutylammonium ion.
(3) Replacement of the chloride ion by a less objectionable ion (e.g., nitrate, alkysulfonate).

Naturally the electrode must also have good electrical properties.

A number of suggested reference electrodes are listed in Table 1.

The calomel electrode mentioned in the description of analytical procedures is either an ordinary calomel electrode or one in which the water in the salt bridge has been replaced by an alcohol.

b. Other Reference Electrodes with Fixed Potentials: the Silver/Silver Chloride Electrode

The silver/silver chloride electrode is less commonly used than the calomel electrode. It has the advantage that it can sometimes be used without a salt bridge (119), although better results are obtained if a salt bridge is used (120). The salt bridge may be a saturated solution of potassium chloride in glacial acetic acid (120), while a solution of silver chloride and lithium chloride in acetic anhydride is recommended for use in absolutely anhydrous media (121).

c. Indicator Electrodes as Reference Electrodes

Any indicator electrode can, in principle, be used as a reference electrode, provided that the activity of the ions to which the electrode responds is kept sufficiently constant throughout the titration. This can be achieved by the use of an indicator electrode that does not respond to the titrant, or, alternatively, the indicator electrode need not be connected directly to the actual reaction medium (as in differential titrations). A particularly elegant form of this second method is that in which the indicator electrode (a metal electrode) is held in contact with the titrant

TABLE 1

MODIFIED CALOMEL ELECTRODES

System	Reference	Notes
$Hg/Hg_2Cl_2/NaCl$ +$NaClO_4$, saturated solution in glacial acetic acid	Bruckenstein and Kolthoff (113)	For precision measurements in glacial acetic acid. Reproducibility $= \pm 0.25$ mv
Commercial calomel electrode filled with a saturated solution of KCl in methanol	Cundiff and Markunas (25)	Specially recommended for the titration of phenols. Fast and reproducible response. Modifications: replacement of the methanol by isopropanol or ethanol. This is the form most commonly used for titrations in nonaqueous media
$Hg/Hg_2Cl_2/LiCl$, saturated solution in ethylenediamine	Gran and Althin (102)	For the titration of weak acids in ethylenediamine. Allow to stand for 1 day before use
$Hg/Hg_2Cl_2/LiClO_4$ in acetic anhydride	Wimer (118b)	For the titration of very weak bases in glacial acetic acid/acetic anhydride
Commercial calomel electrodes filled with a 1 N aqueous solution of tetrabutylammonium chloride	Harlow (89)	Potassium-free electrode Avoids alkali error in the titration of weak acids

emerging from the tip of the buret. This method appears to be generally applicable, and the compactness of the arrangement makes it especially useful for ultramicrodeterminations.

d. Reference Electrodes with Undefined Potentials

The graphite electrode (122, 123) and the silver electrode (124) exhibit very little response to pH changes, and they can therefore be used as reference electrodes. However, the potentials of these electrodes are not very definite, so that they can only be used for titration to the potentiometric break. They are very easy to use. Malmstadt (122) uses the graphite electrode in practically all his automatic titrations.

TABLE 2

INDICATOR ELECTRODES AS REFERENCE ELECTRODES

System	Application	Reference	Notes
Glass electrode	SH function with AgNO₃	Lykken and Teummler (111)	—
Glass electrode	Weak acids with Na methoxide in butylamine	Fritz and Lisicki (87)	Alkali error is so serious that the glass electrode fails to respond
Antimony electrode in the titrant stream	Weak acids in ethylenediamine with Na ethoxide	Moss et al. (107)	—

Chapter 4

REAGENTS

I. Solvents

1. CLASSIFICATION

For practical purposes, the solvents are divided into groups, sometimes in a rather arbitrary manner based mainly on the most common application, the systems being classified as acidic, basic, or neutral. A more logical classification involves only two groups, i.e.,

(i) amphiprotic solvents and
(ii) aprotic solvents.

As noted in Chapter 1; Section I, amphiprotic solvents are those that exhibit appreciable autodissociation, i.e., in which an equilibrium of the type

$$2 \, LH \rightleftharpoons LH_2^+ + L^-$$

exists.

Aprotic solvents do not undergo autodissociation, or at least none is observed, nor is it expected to occur to any appreciable extent. There is probably no clean division between the two groups, since amphiprotic solvents with extremely low K values behave almost as aprotic solvents. The difference is therefore quantitative rather than qualitative.

It is convenient to distinguish between acidic, basic, and neutral members of these groups. This is a purely arbitrary subclassification, since by tacit agreement water is used as the neutrality standard.

Acidic and basic aprotic solvents (the terms are contradictory in themselves) are solvents that can behave either as acids or as bases, although they do not exhibit perceptible autodissociation. Unlike the acidic and basic amphiprotic solvents, they are not appreciably amphoteric. Since these solvents have low acidities and basicities, they exhibit very little leveling.

Amphiprotic solvents:
(a) acidic: acetic acid, formic acid, propionic acid, trifluoroacetic acid, concentrated sulfuric acid, phenol;
(b) basic: ethylenediamine, butylamine, liquid ammonia, benzylamine;
(c) neutral: water, methanol, ethanol, isopropanol, *tert*-butanol, ethylene glycol, ethylene glycol monomethyl ether (methyl cellosolve).

Aprotic solvents:
(a) acidic: nitromethane, nitroethane;
(b) basic: pyridine, dimethylformamide, dimethylsulfoxide;
(c) neutral: dioxane, benzene, xylene, chloroform, acetone,* methyl ethyl ketone,* methyl isobutyl ketone,* nitrobenzene, acetic anhydride,† acetonitrile.

2. THE CHOICE OF SUITABLE SOLVENTS

As noted in Chapter 1, Section II, amphiprotic solvents are only suitable for the titration of acids and bases of very definite strengths. This is true not only of the neutral solvents of this class, but also of the acidic and basic members. These are normally only restricted in one direction, but it is quite possible for acids to be titrated in acidic media and bases in basic media† (strong mineral acids in glacial acetic acid, sodamide in liquid ammonia). In the case of aprotic solvents, there are practically no restrictions on the use of neutral members. However, slight leveling occurs in the acidic and basic members. Protolysis of the neutralization product is also possible, but it is of no importance, since it occurs only if the solvent is badly chosen (e.g., pyridine for the determination of weak bases).

No other restrictions appear to apply to the neutralization process with regard to the solvent. Low polarity of the solvent, though largely suppressing dissociation, does not prevent the components from reacting almost instantaneously. The choice of theoretically suitable solvents is therefore very wide (cf. Figs. 46 and 52).

It must be remembered, however, that unhindered neutralization alone is not enough to guarantee a successful determination. The conditions for a sharp end-point indication must also be satisfied, and the resulting

*Ketones are probably not fully aprotic, but they are included in this group for practical purposes.
†Acetic anhydride does not fit easily into the above scheme. It is amphoteric, but it is also aprotic. Moreover, it enters into chemical reactions with many compounds.

restrictions on the use of solvents are almost as severe as those imposed by protolytic behavior.

The most generally applicable method of end-point detection is potentiometry. Owing to the remarkable versatility of the glass electrode, electrode problems are rare, the most serious difficulties encountered being indication troubles. If the electric equipment involved is of sufficiently high quality, the potentiometric method can be used in any solvent, even inert hydrocarbons (125).

The choice is much more limited in conductometric titrations, since the solvent must be sufficiently polar in this case, the requirements regarding electrical conductivity being higher. However, these effects can be estimated to some extent from theory.

This is rarely possible when indicators are used. In many cases the color change of the indicator is unsatisfactory (particularly with regard to color intensity).

The above list covers the possible interfering factors that limit the practical use of the solvents. In addition to these, the solvent may also react with the substance, but this situation will not be considered here.

Some of the earlier literature attributed considerable importance to the choice of a solvent that increases the acidity or basicity of the substance to be determined; in reality, however, this is not particularly important. Thus the titration of a very weak acid need not be carried out in a strongly basic solvent, though the K_A value of the acid in such a medium is undoubtedly much higher than in an aprotic solvent, owing to the tendency towards salt formation. The deciding factor (aside from basicity of the titrant) is not the absolute K_A value, but its ratio to that of the solvent; in other words, the acidity of the solvent must be sufficiently low to prevent protolysis. In the case of amphiprotic solvents, this effect is best achieved by the use of a strongly basic solvent. This is unnecessary in the case of aprotic solvents, however, since sharp end-point detections can be achieved even in perfectly neutral (inert) solvents.

A number of other points must be considered in the choice of a solvent for the simultaneous determination of acids or bases having different strengths. Leveling is acceptable only to a very small extent. For a sharp potentiometric determination of two acids or bases, the pK values must differ by at least about three to four units, and the fully useful range of the solvent must accordingly be greater than for a single determination. This is particularly noticeable in the case of solvents with relatively high dissociation constants, i.e., especially acidic amphiprotic solvents. These can only be used for the determination of total basicities. Neutral and basic amphiprotic solvents are much more suitable for simultaneous determinations, owing to their lower K values. The most suitable of all, however, are aprotic solvents, which have an almost unlimited pH scale.

Even when the above points are considered, the number of possible solvents for simultaneous determinations is still quite large. The most suitable of these can be found either by empirical tests or on the basis of the influence of the solvent on the strengths of acids and bases. The rules concerning the influence of the dielectric constant are particularly important.

The solvent should also suppress, as far as possible, any tendency of the substances to associate (in the case of acids), since association leads to a steep potential curve and hence to greater difficulty of separation (see Chapter 1, Section IV,1). Amphiprotic solvents are again more suitable from this point of view, owing to their tendency towards hydrogen-bond formation. The best compromise appears to be *tert*-butanol, which occupies a position between amphiprotic and aprotic solvents (cf. Fig. 53).

In addition to the more theoretical requirements, the solvent must have a sufficiently high solvent power. While this requirement can usually be readily satisfied in the determination of concentrations, i.e., when the size of the sample is relatively small, difficulties are often encountered in trace determinations in which large samples are used. Difficulties of this nature can often be avoided by the use of mixed solvents; in this case the substance should preferably be dissolved first in the better solvent, the resulting solution then being diluted with the poorer solvent. The advantage of this procedure is that, even when the solubility of the substance in the mixture is too low, it often remains in solution long enough to enable the titration to be carried out, owing to supersaturation. Moreover, the time taken for dissolution is reduced.

A guide to the choice of solvents is given in Table 3.

3. DISCUSSION OF INDIVIDUAL SOLVENTS

a. Amphiprotic Solvents, Acidic

α. *Glacial Acetic Acid.* Glacial acetic acid was the first organic solvent to be used in the determination of weak bases (126–130), and even today it is still regarded as the best solvent for the determination of total base. The end point is determined either potentiometrically or with the aid of indicators.

TABLE 3
SOLVENTS WITH PARTICULARLY GOOD SOLVENT POWER

Sample	Solvent	Notes
a. For acidimetric titrations		
Hydrocarbons	Chlorobenzene/glacial acetic acid 1:1	Leveling
	Methyl isobutyl ketone	Nonleveling, but less suitable than chlorobenzene/ glacial acetic acid for very weak bases
Acrylonitrile copolymers	Formic acid/nitromethane approx. 1:40	Ref. (409)
Salts	Glacial acetic acid/water	Dissolve first in the minimum of water. Acetic anhydride may be added
	G-H mixtures	Dissolve first in glycol
Polymers	Tetrahydrofuran, possibly with additives	Unsuitable for very weak bases
Polyamides	*m*-Cresol/isopropanol 2:1	Ref. (410)
b. For alkalimetric titrations		
Hydrocarbons	Methyl isobutyl ketone	—
	Pyridine	—
Polymers	Dimethylformamide	—
Salts	Ethylenediamine	Salt may be dissolved
	Dimethylformamide	first in a little water
Difficultly soluble acids, e.g., terephthalic acid	Dimethylformamide	—
Polyamides	Propargyl alcohol	Ref. (410)

Commercial glacial acetic acid anal. grade can be used without prior purification. Its water content is usually of the order of from 0.1 to 0.4% (determination by the K. Fischer method). This quantity does not interfere with most determinations. If perfectly anhydrous acetic acid is required for special purposes (e.g., in the case of very weak bases), excess acetic anhydride may be added, or if this causes interference, the solvent may be purified by the Eichelberger–La Mer procedure (131). This consists in treatment of the acid with chromium trioxide and triacetyl borate, followed by fractionation. According to Bruckenstein (132), the treatment with triacetyl borate may be replaced by fractional distillation with benzene. The water content of the product obtained in this way is less

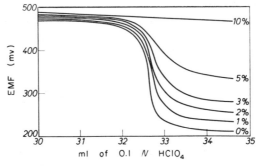

FIG. 26. The effect of water content on the titration of bases in glacial acetic acid with perchloric acid. [Pifer and Wollish (134).]

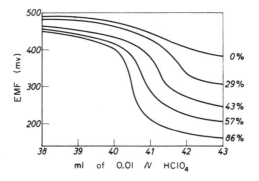

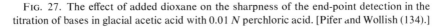

FIG. 27. The effect of added dioxane on the sharpness of the end-point detection in the titration of bases in glacial acetic acid with 0.01 N perchloric acid. [Pifer and Wollish (134).]

than 0.02%. It should always be borne in mind that certain amines, particularly aniline, are extremely readily acetylated, so that even very small quantities of anhydride can cause severe interference. Even perfectly anhydrous acetic acid may be unsuitable in this respect, and can lead to acetylation (133).

The effect of water on the sharpness of the potentiometric break is shown in Fig. 26.

It can be seen that the water content should not be higher than 1%. The sharpness of the break can be further improved by the addition of non-polar aprotic solvents. The effect of added dioxane is shown in Fig. 27.

The addition of such a solvent is particularly advantageous for titrations in dilute solutions using indicators, since the sharpness of the color change is greatly improved (135).

Glacial acetic acid can be used as a nonleveling solvent in the determination of very strong acids (136). The titrant used in this case is pyridine or dimethylaniline in glacial acetic acid.

β. *Formic Acid.* This is a stronger acid than glacial acetic acid, mainly because of its high dielectric constant, and it is used especially for the titration of very weak bases (urea, caffeine) (137). The water content may be from 1 to 2%. The storage life does not appear to be very good and bottles that have been opened can no longer be used after storage for a few weeks (135).

The end point is detected potentiometrically, since no suitable color indicators have been found. Crystal violet in particular is quite unsuitable, since it gives a green solution in formic acid owing to the high acidity of the latter.

γ. *Propionic Acid.* Little use has been made of this solvent so far. It is reported to be even less basic than glacial acetic acid (138). Caffeine and urea have been determined on the micro scale in this solvent (with added acetic anhydride) (135).

δ. *Phenol.* Pure phenol cannot be used as a solvent, owing to its high melting point, but it is of interest as an additive. A phenol-chloroform-acetonitrile mixture is recommended as a solvent for the determination of salts of organic bases, because of its high solvent power (139).

ε. *Trifluoroacetic Acid.* This solvent could be of interest for the determination of very weak bases when acetic anhydride cannot be used owing to the danger of acetylation. It can be used as the solvent for the determination of urea and thiourea. The end point is detected potentiometrically with platinum electrodes, one of which is held in the stream of titrant (140). It is purified (and recovered) by distillation of an azeotrope with 30% of water, followed by drying with phosphorus pentoxide and fractionation.

b. Amphiprotic Solvents, Basic

α. *Ethylenediamine.* Ethylenediamine was the first strongly basic solvent to be used in the titration of weak acids (141). It levels strong acids, but carboxylic acids and phenols can be determined in the presence of one another. The end point is detected potentiometrically or by means of color indicators.

In spite of these favorable properties, ethylenediamine has a number of serious practical disadvantages. It fumes in air, is toxic and caustic (particularly dangerous to the eyes), and rapidly absorbs water and carbon dioxide from the air. This last disadvantage is so serious that blank determinations are unreliable. To obtain a sharp end point, particularly in the determination of phenols, the ethylenediamine must be dried (maximum water content 1%). The monohydrate, which is relatively easily obtainable, cannot be decomposed by distillation. It may be repeatedly dried over potassium hydroxide until the latter shows no sign of the action of water, and then distilled over sodium. A simpler method is by azeotropic distillation with benzene (142).

β. *Butylamine.* This solvent has properties similar to those of ethylenediamine, but it is cheaper and easier to dry. Its solvent power is lower than that of ethylenediamine. If the result of a blank determination is sufficiently low, the solvent can be used directly; otherwise it must be distilled over potassium hydroxide before use.

γ. *Benzylamine.* This is similar to butylamine, but has less odor and is a more powerful solvent.

c. Amphiprotic Solvents, Neutral

α. *Primary Monoalcohols (Methanol, Ethanol, etc.).* These solvents have almost the same acidity or basicity as water, and differ from the latter mainly in their lower dielectric constants. Thus with regard to the titration of weak acids and bases, their range of use is no wider than that of water. However, the lower dielectric constant permits the determination of the two carboxyl groups of dicarboxylic acids in the presence of one another, and the titration of amino acids in the betaine form (see Chapter 1, Section IV). They also offer advantages over water with regard to their solvent power.

The end point is best detected potentiometrically, since color changes are not too satisfactory.

β. Isopropanol. Secondary alcohols are weaker acids than primary alcohols (143). Isopropanol is therefore preferable to primary alcohols. Although phenol cannot be determined in pure isopropanol, a much higher concentration of alcohol (e.g., in the titrant solution) can be tolerated.

Isopropanol has good solvent properties, particularly for hydrocarbons, and can act as a solubilizing agent between these and water. It can therefore be used to advantage for the determination of acid values in oils. It can be obtained in a very pure state, and requires no further treatment.

Isopropanol can be used as a component of so-called G-H mixtures (see diols, Section I,3,*c*,δ).

γ. tert-Butanol. The acidity of tertiary alcohols is so low that these can almost be regarded as aprotic solvents. They are therefore very suitable for use in the titration of weak acids. A special advantage of this solvent is the fact that the hydroxyl groups prevent any association that might result from hydrogen bonding, so giving flat potential curves and permitting a better separation of the potential plateaus due to substances with different acidities. *tert*-Butanol was first used by Fritz and Marple (144), and has all the properties of a future standard solvent for the stepwise titration of acids, particularly of weak acids (down to the acidity of phenols). Its separating action is much better than that of acetone, though not quite so good as that of pyridine. Many indicators are suitable for use in this solvent (Fig. 28).

The compound can be obtained in the pure form and gives practically no blank value. It can be purified, if necessary, by fractionation over potassium hydroxide or sodium. Owing to the high melting point of this solvent (25.8°C), it is recommended that 5% of benzene should be added, since this lowers the melting point to about 16°C.

δ. Diols. Palit (146) introduced diols (ethylene glycol, 1,2-propylene glycol) as carrier components in G-H (glycol-hydrocarbon) mixtures. They are intermediate between neutral and acidic amphiprotic solvents, being less basic than water but much more basic than glacial acetic acid. An important advantage of these solvents over glacial acetic acid is their higher polarity, which makes them much more powerful solvents for salts. Because of their undesirably high viscosities, they are used as mixtures (generally in the ratio of 1:1) with an aromatic hydrocarbon, chloroform, or isopropanol.

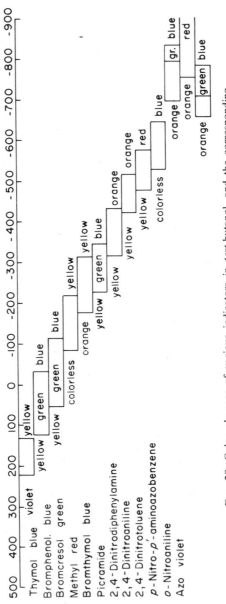

Fig. 28. Color changes of various indicators in *tert*-butanol, and the corresponding potentials of a glass electrode against a saturated calomel electrode. [Marple and Fritz (145).]

G-H mixtures are useful for the determination of inorganic salts of weak acids with strong bases. They can also, in theory, be used for the determination of weakly basic amines, but these determinations are better carried out in other solvents.

ε. *Ethylene Glycol Monomethyl Ether (Methyl Glycol, Methyl Cellosolve)*. This solvent was recently used for the first time by Ruch *et al.* (147, 148). It has weakly basic properties, and can therefore be used for the determination of weak bases. A special advantage of titations in this solvent is that they are not subject to interference due to any buffering substances present [e.g., a large excess of carbonamide in the determination of small quantities of tertiary amines in other amines by the addition of acetic anhydride (148)].

d. Aprotic Solvents, Acidic

α. *Nitromethane*. Nitromethane is a very weak acid (comparable to phenol), but exhibits practically no basic properties. Owing to its relatively high polarity, which favors the ionization of salts, it has recently been used for the determination of bases, and particularly of those with very low basicities (149, 150). Mixtures with other solvents are especially useful; e.g., mixtures with acetic anhydride give sharper end points (149), while mixtures with dioxane/glacial acetic acid/acetic anhydride are valuable for very special simultaneous determinations (151).

β. *Nitroethane*. This solvent can be used as a substitute for nitromethane, which is sometimes difficult to obtain owing to explosion hazards. The properties of nitroethane are even slightly better than those of nitromethane (152), and purification is not required in the case of high-grade commercial products.

e. Aprotic Solvents, Basic

α. *Pyridine*. Pyridine is a very useful solvent for the determination of various acids. However, it has the disadvantages of an unpleasant odor and a relatively high price.

The leveling action of pyridine is surprisingly slight, probably because of its low polarity. Only the strongest of the mineral acids, such as perchloric and hydrochloric acids and the first proton of sulfuric acid, are leveled. The second proton of sulfuric acid, on the other hand, is quite distinct from the first (Chapter 1, Section IV,1). The leveling effect decreases with the strength of the acid, so that pyridine is perfectly suit-

able for the determination of carboxylic acids and phenols. However, it
is generally necessary to take into account a small blank titer. The value
of this solvent for simultaneous determinations is illustrated in Fig. 29.

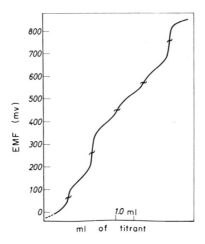

FIG. 29. Titration of a mixture of nitric, maleic, and acetic acids and phenol with 0.1 N
tetrabutylammonium hydroxide. The potential jumps follow one another in the order:
nitric acid, maleic acid (1st stage), acetic acid, maleic acid (2nd stage), phenol. Solvent:
pyridine. Glass/calomel electrodes. [Cundiff and Markunas (153).]

Owing to its low dielectric constant, pyridine is particularly suitable
for the determination of polybasic acids, the individual functions of which
are clearly separated (153). A special advantage of this solvent in comparison with others of theoretically similar efficiency is the complete absence of any reactivity with strong acids, which makes it possible to obtain very accurate results (154).

Pyridine is purified by distillation over barium oxide. If particularly
high purity is required, the resulting solvent is then refluxed for 3 hr over
fresh barium oxide and finally distilled over a column; atmospheric carbon dioxide and moisture must be excluded. Purification via the sparingly
soluble perchlorate is dangerous, and should therefore be avoided.

β. *Dimethylformamide.* This solvent possesses very distinct advantages and disadvantages. Its advantages are its ready availability in
a satisfactory degree of purity, its excellent solvent power, particularly
for polar compounds, its freedom from odor and toxicity, and the wide

applicability resulting from its good solvent properties. An important disadvantage, however, is its relatively high reactivity. This is particularly noticeable in the determination of strong acids. Although the correct total titer is obtained, the ratio of the first and second stages of sulfuric acid is subject to an error of up to 20% (154). In the determination of weak and very weak acids, the correct results were obtained, but only when the system was free from water. Thus any water introduced with the substance to be determined gives excessively high values as a result of hydrolysis. Moreover, titrant solutions containing alcohols (e.g., potassium methoxide in methanol/benzene) interfere with the end point to a greater extent in dimethylformamide than, e.g., in ethylenediamine. For a sharp indicator end point in the titration of phenols, the methanol content should not exceed about 2 to 4% (155).

The basicity of dimethylformamide is even lower than that of pyridine, so that it can almost be regarded as a neutral solvent. Thus strongly basic amines, such as butylamine, in dimethylformamide can be titrated with perchloric acid in dioxane. Aromatic amines with pK_B values of about 9, on the other hand, can no longer be determined.

Titrations in dimethylformamide can be carried out either by potentiometric methods or with the aid of color indicators. It is necessary to take a blank titer into account, particularly in the determination of very weak acids. Nevertheless, purification is generally not required, and may even lead to an increase in the quantity of impurities present. For special applications, the solvent may be passed through a mixed-bed ion exchanger and then treated with activated alumina. Fractionation *in vacuo* is also effective, since impurities that appear to be readily hydrolyzable are eliminated.

γ. *Dimethylsulfoxide.* This solvent has so far found little use, but it appears to be suitable for many applications (156). Its properties are formally similar to those of dimethylformamide, but it does not suffer from the ease of hydrolysis of the latter. On the other hand, dimethylsulfoxide can act as an oxidizing or reducing agent. It reacts explosively with strong perchloric acid (156a).

f. Aprotic Solvents, Neutral

α. *Ketones.* The literature contains descriptions of the use of three ketones, namely acetone, methyl ethyl ketone, and methyl isobutyl ketone. These solvents do not differ greatly in their properties. Some disagreement exists as to their respective merits. The present author has found that acetone gives the sharpest end point in the determination of phenols; for this reason, and because of the ready availability and moderate price of pure acetone, this solvent appears to offer special advantages. Methyl ethyl ketone has been particularly recommended for the determination of bases with perchloric acid (157); however, acetone is also very suitable for this determination.

Ketones are almost perfectly aprotic, neutral solvents of medium polarity; in principle, therefore, they are of general use. Their basicity is slightly higher than that of glacial acetic acid. However, their reactivity imposes certain restrictions in the determination of strong acids. Acetone

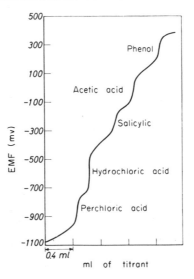

Fig. 30. Simultaneous titration of five different acids with tetrabutylammonium hydroxide in methyl isobutyl ketone.

and methyl isobutyl ketone react with the first stage of sulfuric acid though not to quite such a marked extent as does dimethylformamide. The error due to this reaction is of the order of 2%, and can therefore be ignored in some cases (154). The ketones can theoretically react with primary amines to form condensation products (Schiff bases) (158), but it appears from the author's experiments with aniline (which is known to be particularly reactive) that this does not affect the titration. However, interference may occur with other compounds of this type.

Ketones, particularly methyl isobutyl ketone, give good titration curves for the determination of mixtures of acids. Since there is little leveling, even mineral acids can be largely distinguished from one another (Figs. 30 and 31).

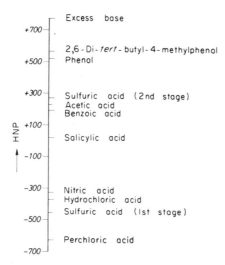

FIG. 31. Half-neutralization potentials HNP of various acids in methyl isobutyl ketone. Titrant: tetrabutylammonium hydroxide. [Bruss and Wyld (159).]

A surprising point in Fig. 31 is the fact that the second stage of sulfuric acid has a lower acidity than normal carboxylic acids. Ketones are valuable solvents for the simultaneous determination of carboxylic acids and phenols. In addition to their ready availability and inoffensive odor, they give practically no blank titer. Atmospheric carbon dioxide is absorbed so slowly that the determinations can, if necessary, be carried out in open vessels and without a protective gas.

The author's experiments indicate that no purification is necessary. Small quantities of weak acids in methyl ethyl ketone and methyl isobutyl ketone can be removed by passage through a column packed with activated alumina (159).

The end point is usually determined potentiometrically.

β. *Acetonitrile.* This solvent was first used for the simultaneous determination of amines with different basicities (160). However, it can also be used for the titration of acids of various strengths, as well as for redox reactions. The end point is detected potentiometrically or by means of color indicators.

Acidic and basic impurities can be removed by passage through a column packed with activated alumina. A more effective method involves treatment with calcium hydride, distillation over phosphorus pentoxide, and finally fractionation over calcium hydride (161). Bases and water can be removed simply by distillation over phosphorus pentoxide.

Acetonitrile has a remarkable effect on certain heavy metal salts. The acetates of copper, nickel, etc., cannot be titrated as bases, even in non-basic solvents. This titration can, however, be carried out in acetonitrile, evidently because of complex formation with these metals, which are known to form cyanide complexes (162).

γ. *Nitrobenzene.* This solvent permits an excellent differentiation (163) between amines of various basicities on titration with perchloric acid in dioxane. The end point is found potentiometrically.

δ. *Solvents with the Ether Linkages.* This group includes diethyl ether, dioxane, tetrahydrofuran, and ethylene glycol dimethyl ether. These solvents are mainly used as diluents. Potentiometric titrations with normal equipment can only be carried out in tetrahydrofuran and in ethylene glycol dimethyl ether, since the electrical resistances of solutions in ether and dioxane are too high.

The ethers often contain peroxides, which behave as more or less strongly acidic impurities. The solvents are purified by distillation over clean sodium. In the case of dioxane, treatment with a strongly acidic cation exchanger is recommended to prevent the solvent from turning brown in the presence of perchloric acid (when dioxane is used as the solvent for this acid). A more effective procedure consists in refluxing for several hours with 5% concentrated hydrochloric acid, neutralization with 50% potassium hydroxide solution, drying over potassium hydroxide, and distillation over sodium.

The ethers are much more strongly basic than glacial acetic acid, and cannot be used for the determination of very weak bases.

ε. *Hydrocarbons and Chlorinated Hydrocarbons.* These compounds are generally used only as nonpolar diluents. Direct potentiometric and even conductometric titrations can be carried out in these solvents, but only under certain conditions; on the other hand, color indicators can be used. It should be noted that chloroform normally contains 1% of alcohol, which is added as a stabilizer. It can be removed by treatment with activated alumina or with concentrated sulfuric acid.

ζ. Acetic Anhydride. There are two reasons for the use of acetic anhydride:

(a) For the complete removal of water in the titration of very weak bases, leading to a substantial improvement in the sharpness of the potentiometric breaks. Apart from the elimination of the protolytic action of water, this improvement is also due partly to a special effect. The strongest acid that can exist in acetic anhydride is the acetyl cation (164), which is more strongly acidic than the acetonium ion $CH_3COOH_2^+$:

$$CH_3COOCOCH_3 + HClO_4 \leftrightarrows CH_3CO^+ + ClO_4^- + CH_3COOH$$

For this reason any acetic acid present has a buffering action during the determination of very weak bases in acetic anhydride. The acetic acid content should therefore be kept as low as possible, though up to 10% causes no significant interference (Fig. 32).

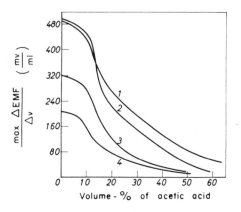

FIG. 32. The sharpness of the end-point detection, expressed as the maximum change in potential per unit volume of titrant at the equivalence point, as a function of the concentration of acetic acid. Potentiometric titrations in acetic anhydride with perchloric acid. 1, thioacetamide; 2, *N*-acetylpiperidine; 3, *N*-formylpyrrolidine; 4, *N,N*-dimethylformamide. [Wimer (165).]

The high reactivity of the acetyl cation can give rise to side reactions. This ion is known to react with amides of α,β-unsaturated carboxylic acids (e.g., acrylamide), so preventing the quantitative determination of these compounds (165).

(b) As an auxiliary solvent in the determination of tertiary amines. The acetic anhydride acetylates primary and secondary amines, which consequently lose most of their basicity, and are not included in the determination under the conditions used.

Acetic anhydride is obtainable in a very pure state, and further purification is unnecessary.

II. Color Indicators

1. INDICATOR DYES AND THEIR USES

The number of indicator dyes that have been described in the literature is immense, and no attempt will be made in the present book to give even a moderately complete account of them. Moreover, their use in many cases is very specific, and limited to certain solvents. We shall therefore confine our discussion to well-proven and commonly used indicators.

No thought need be given to the choice of indicator in the case of systems that are well-known from the literature. Caution is required, however, in the titration of a substance whose determination has not yet been described. Homologs of known compounds do not generally differ significantly in their pK values. In cases of doubt, or where sufficient information cannot be obtained from analogy, a potentiometric check should be carried out. This is best done with the aid of a recording instrument. The indicator is added to the solution, and the color changes are noted continuously on the instrument chart while the curve is being recorded. The sample need not be weighed out accurately for this check. The suitability of the indicator, as well as of the solvent, can be accurately estimated from the resulting diagram. Difficulties may arise in the case of a very nonpolar solvent, in which potentiometric checks are scarcely possible; the check must then be carried out in the usual manner with weighed samples of test substances.

The color hue at the end point is not always exactly the same for different substances, owing to their different pK values (166). In titration with dilute solutions, therefore, it is necessary to use color standards. These are used in any case for microdeterminations, in order to find the end point with greater accuracy.

2. Discussion of the Individual Color Indicators

a. Indicators for the Determination of Bases

α. Crystal Violet (Methyl Violet)

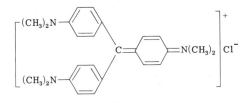

Crystal violet

Methyl violet is a mixture of less highly methylated derivatives. Its behavior is practically the same as that of crystal violet, but it is less intensely colored, and must therefore be used in higher concentrations (167). For this reason, it is preferable to use crystal violet.

Crystal violet has two color-change regions, but these lie so close together that only the first color change is generally used. The end point is taken as the transition from violet to a pure blue (the color of the singly protonated form). The double protonated form is yellow, so that, if the titration is carried too far, the pure blue first changes to the mixed color green.

As was mentioned above, the color change in glacial acetic acid is made appreciably sharper by the addition of an inert solvent. Figure 33 shows the end points observed in a 1:3 glacial acetic acid/chloroform mixture during a microtitration with 0.01 N perchloric acid in dioxane.

It is particularly desirable in microtitrations to titrate against a comparison color, since the end point cannot otherwise be detected with sufficient sharpness. According to Gutterson and Ma (168), the color standards can be prepared by the addition of perchloric acid to a solution of the indicator in the titration solvent till the color changes to pure blue. However, a solution of this type has a very low buffer capacity, and its stability is therefore very poor. It is consequently preferable to use the comparison solutions developed by Belcher (167) for ultramicrodeterminations. The end point is a pure blue. However, at high salt concentrations (in the sample), the end point shifts towards blue-green. This also occurs in the titration of relatively weak bases. This reduces the sharpness of the end-point detection, and is used to check whether it is permissible to use a given color standard for the substance in question.

Blue reference solution: Urea (100 mg) is dissolved in 70 to 80 ml of glacial acetic acid; 3.3 ml of 0.01% crystal violet solution in glacial acetic acid and 3 ml of 0.10 N perchloric acid are added, and the solution is made up to 100 ml.

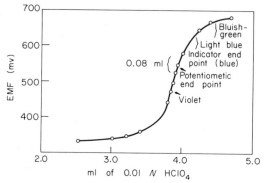

FIG. 33. Potentiometric check on the indicator color change in the titration of potassium biphthalate in 1:3 glacial acetic acid/chloroform with 0.01 N perchloric acid. Indicator: crystal violet. [Gutterson and Ma (168).]

Blue-green reference solution: As above, but with 6 ml of 0.10 N perchloric acid instead of 3 ml.

Crystal violet is probably the most widely used of all indicators in the determination of bases. It can be used in very many solvents, but naturally not in those with basic properties. In addition to glacial acetic acid, these include: acetic anhydride, nitromethane, acetonitrile, benzene, chloroform, and dioxane, as well as mixtures of these solvents. However, even neutralizations in acid chlorides such as thionyl chloride and phosphorus oxychloride have been studied with the aid of crystal violet (169).

The indicator solution is generally a 0.1% solution of crystal violet in glacial acetic acid. A saturated, filtered solution in chlorobenzene may be used in aprotic solvents.

β. Malachite Green. Like crystal violet, this is a triphenylmethane dye. The color changes from a bluish green to yellow. The color change occurs at somewhat lower pH values than in the case of crystal violet, so that malachite green is particularly suitable for the determination of weak bases (e.g., opium alkaloids). For this reason it is mainly used in acetic anhydride. Concentration used: 0.1% in glacial acetic acid.

γ. *α-Naphtholbenzein*

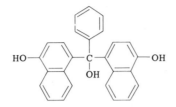

This compound has two widely separated color-change ranges. It can therefore be used for the determination of weak acids in benzene/isopropanol. The color changes from yellow to green, then to blue-green in the alkaline range. Its uses are similar to those of crystal violet, and the color change is much more distinct. α-Naphtholbenzein is mentioned very frequently in American literature. Concentration used: 0.1% in glacial acetic acid or isopropanol.

δ. *Neutral Red.* This is an azine dye, which is used in acetic anhydride for the titration of very weak bases (caffeine). The color change is from pink to blue.

ε. *Triphenylcarbinol.* This is used for the same purposes as neutral red. The color change is from colorless to yellow, the color of the triphenylmethyl cation.

ζ. *Dibenzalacetone.* This is used for the titration of very weak bases such as urea, in acetic anhydride. The color change is from colorless to yellow.

η. *Quinaldine Red.* This indicator is rather more strongly basic than crystal violet. It can therefore be used in some cases for the selective determination of strong bases in glacial acetic acid in the presence of weaker bases (hydrochlorides). The color change is from red to colorless, and is particularly easy to detect. For this reason, quinaldine red can be advantageously used in general for the determination of substances that act as strong bases in glacial acetic acid.

θ. *Eosin.* This particularly basic indicator can be used for the titration of strongly basic aliphatic amines in acetonitrile in the presence of aromatic amines (170). The color changes sharply from pink with a green fluorescence to yellowish-colorless.

ι. *Dimethyl Yellow (Butter Yellow, p-Dimethylaminoazobenzene).*
This indicator, which is used in aqueous solutions (color change between
pH 2.9 and 4.0), can also be used in nonaqueous solutions in certain
special cases (e.g., titration of bases in G-H mixtures). Addition of 10%
methylene blue leads to a mixed indicator (analogous to the Tashiro
indicator) in which the original red-yellow color change becomes a violet-
green change. A pure gray is obtained at the end point.

b. Indicators for the Determination of Acids

α. *Thymol Blue*

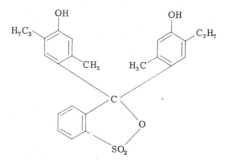

This sulfonphthalein is widely used in the determination of carboxylic
acids and compounds of similar acidity. The very sharp color change is
from yellow to blue. The choice of solvents is relatively wide, and includes dimethylformamide, butylamine, pyridine, acetone, alcohols,
benzene, and acetonitrile. However, this indicator cannot be used in
ethylenediamine.

Thymol blue has a second color change in the relatively acidic range.
This change can be used for the determination of strong mineral acids in
the presence of carboxylic acids (in isopropanol). The color change is
from red to yellow, then to blue in the alkaline range.

The indicator is used as a 0.2% solution in dioxane.

β. *Azo Violet (p-Nitrophenylazoresorcinol).* This indicator is a valuable supplement to thymol blue. It is somewhat less acidic, and is therefore more suitable than the latter for the determination of particularly
weak carboxylic acids (and of strongly acidic phenols). It can be used
in ethylenediamine, but not in benzene or ether. Other solvents in which

it can be used include pyridine, butylamine, and dimethylformamide. The color change is from red to blue, and the indicator is used either as a saturated solution in benzene or as a 0.5% solution in pyridine.

Azo violet also has a second color change (yellow to red) in the acidic range which can be used for the separate determination of mineral acids in pyridine (171).

γ. *Phenolphthalein and Thymolphthalein.* These indicators are often used in aqueous systems, and their use in alcohol is also well-known (saponification values, etc.). They have the disadvantage that the color change in organic solvents is often difficult to recognize, owing to the low color intensity. However, this is not the case in dimethylformamide, in which the color change is extremely sharp and easy to observe.

δ. *Cresol Red.* A mixture of cresol red and thymol blue has certain advantages over phenolphthalein in the determination of OH values by acetylation (172).

ε. *o-Nitroaniline.* The acidic properties of this dye are extremely weak, and it can therefore be used for the determination of very weak acids (phenols). The solvents used are ethylenediamine and dimethylformamide. The color change, which is from yellow to orange-red, is unfortunately not very sharp. Potentiometric checks show that it occurs a little too early in the determination of phenols, and the titration should therefore be continued to a distinct orange-red. The indicator is used as a 1% solution in benzene.

ζ. *p-Hydroxyazobenzene.* This indicator is suitable for the titration of carboxylic acids in ethylenediamine and in dimethylformamide. The color change is from pale yellow to an intense yellow. After the end point has been reached, *o*-nitroaniline may be added and the titration continued to the new end point; it is possible in this way to determine carboxylic acids and phenols in the presence of one another. *p*-Hydroxyazobenzene is used as a 0.1% solution in benzene.

η. *p-Phenylaminoazobenzene.* This dye, which has an extremely low acidity, can be used as the indicator in the direct titration of alcohols with very strong bases (lithium aluminum amide). It can be prepared by coupling of diazotized aniline with diphenylamine. The color change is from yellow to violet (0.1% in benzene).

III. Titrant Solutions

1. STANDARD ACIDS

Perchloric acid is used almost exclusively, because of its outstanding acid strength. Each of the solvents used, i.e., dioxane and glacial acetic acid, has its own advantages and disadvantages.

Dioxane gives sharper potentiometric breaks in most determinations (173). In the simultaneous determination of bases having different strengths, little or no acetic acid can be tolerated because of its leveling action. On the other hand, the solution cannot be kept absolutely anhydrous (except by the use of anhydrous perchloric acid, which is dangerous), with the result that the titration of very weak bases becomes very slightly more difficult. This difficulty may also be due to the greater basicity of dioxane in comparison with glacial acetic acid.

Perchloric acid in glacial acetic acid with added acetic anhydride provides an anhydrous reagent suitable for the titration of very weak bases (amides, Fig. 34).

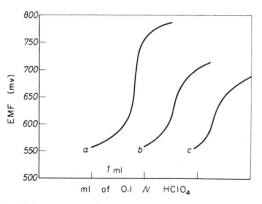

FIG. 34. Titration of the very weak base lithium nitrate with perchloric acid: *a,* in glacial acetic acid/acetic anhydride; *b,* in glacial acetic acid; *c,* in glacial acetic acid, perchloric acid in dioxane. [Fritz and Fulda (149).]

On the whole, a dioxane solution is preferable and, apart from the limitations noted above, universally applicable. It must be borne in mind, however, that the addition of dioxane causes a change in the composition of the solvent. This is an advantage in the case of glacial acetic acid, since it increases the sharpness of the potentiometric break, but it is also possible that, in some cases, the introduction of large quantities of dioxane may have undesirable results.

There are a number of special cases in which perchloric acid cannot be used. This is the case if mucilaginous precipitates of perchlorates are formed during the titration, since these can affect the response of the glass electrode. (Crystalline precipitates such as potassium perchlorate are generally harmless.) This trouble can be avoided by the replacement of perchloric acid by an alkylsulfonic acid (174) or by diphenylphosphoric acid (175), which form soluble salts. However, these compounds are weaker acids, and so cannot be used for the titration of very weak bases.

It was recently suggested (176) that trifluoromethylsulfonic acid should be used. This acid is as strong as perchloric acid, and does not give insoluble products, but it is unfortunately difficult to obtain. The same is true of fluorosulfonic acid (177).

The titrants are nearly always used as 0.1 N solutions. However, 0.01 N and 0.001 N solutions are occasionally used in microtitrations (168, 178, 179); these can be easily prepared by dilution of 0.1 N solutions.

The solutions are not usually adjusted to an accurate concentration; instead, correction factors are generally used.

Preparation of an 0.1 N Solution of Perchloric Acid in Dioxane

Reagents:
  72% perchloric acid anal. grade
  Dioxane, anhydrous (for purification, see Section I,3,f,δ)

  Approximately 8.5 ml (14.5 gm) of perchloric acid are dissolved in 1 liter of dioxane.

Preparation of an 0.1 N Solution of
Perchloric Acid in Glacial Acetic Acid

Reagents:
  72% perchloric acid anal. grade
  Glacial acetic acid, anhydrous
  Acetic anhydride, pure

  Approximately 8.5 ml (14.5 gm) of perchloric acid are dissolved in about 900 ml of glacial acetic acid. Enough acetic anhydride is added to react with the water (the added perchloric acid requires about 8.8 ml, i.e., 7.5 gm), and the solution is made up to 1 liter with glacial acetic acid.
  A small excess or a small deficiency of acetic anhydride may be used according to the particular application. The solution is allowed to

stand for 1 day before use. The titer of an 0.1 N solution in acetic acid has been found to remain unchanged for 9 months, whereas an 0.01 N solution had to be restandardized after from 1 to 2 months.

Preparation of an 0.1 N Solution of Alkylsulfonic Acid in Glacial Acetic Acid

Reagents:

Methanesulfonic, ethanesulfonic, or *p*-toluenesulfonic acid, as pure and free from water as possible

Glacial acetic acid

Acetic anhydride

A suitable quantity of the sulfonic acid is dissolved in about 900 ml of glacial acetic acid, and the theoretical quantity of acetic anhydride is added to react with the water. The solution is then made up to 1 liter and allowed to stand for 1 day.

Note: If the titration is to be carried out at very low temperatures ($<0°C$) glacial acetic acid and dioxane cannot be used, because of their relatively high melting points. Ethylene glycol diethyl ether is used as the solvent (180).

Standardization of Standard Acids

The substances normally used for the standardization of the solutions are:

Potassium hydrogen phthalate (166) ($KHC_8H_4O_4$; equivalent weight 204.22)

This compound is obtainable in a very pure state and requires no further purification. It is practically nonhygroscopic. Up to 0.2% of water may be present, but this is removed by drying to constant weight at 135°C. One disadvantage of this compound is the fact that it must be dissolved in hot glacial acetic acid. Moreover, with perchloric acid it forms potassium perchlorate, which may (depending on the solvent) form a mucilaginous precipitate and interfere with the operation of the glass electrode. Pure glacial acetic acid is therefore the most suitable solvent. The end point can be found either potentiometrically or with the aid of indicators.

Sodium carbonate anhydrous (Na_2CO_3; equivalent weight 41.50)

Sodium carbonate is also obtainable in a very pure state. It may be dried at 350°C to drive off the last traces of water. For use in standardization, the soda must be dissolved in glacial acetic acid. It is advantageous that no precipitate forms in the course of the titration. The end point may be found either potentiometrically or by means of indicators.

Diphenylguanidine [$(C_6H_5NH)_2CNH$; equivalent weight 211.26]

The commercial product must be purified before use by washing with cold toluene followed by recrystallization three times from the same solvent. It is then dried at 100°C.

Tris(hydroxymethyl)aminomethane [$(CH_2OH)_3CNH_2$; equivalent weight 121.14]

This compound has recently been favored. It is obtainable in an excellent state of purity. The only restriction on its use is that there must be no acetic anhydride present, since this tends to acetylate the base.

2. STANDARD BASES

Quaternary ammonium bases have now become largely established for potentiometric titrations, except where there are special arguments against their use. Their advantages over alkali metal alkoxide solutions are:

(1) avoidance of the alkali error of the glass electrode,
(2) avoidance of sparingly soluble salts of alkali metals.

Their disadvantages are a relatively high cost and the fact that their preparation is tedious. The most widely used of these bases is tetrabutylammonium hydroxide. This compound is generally prepared by shaking a solution of the iodide in methanol with silver oxide (153). An equimolar mixture of the alkoxide and the hydroxide is formed (181) in accordance with the equation:

$$2(C_4H_9)_4NI + Ag_2O + CH_3OH \rightarrow (C_4H_9)_4NOH + (C_4H_9)_4NOCH_3 + 2AgI$$

Owing to its amphiprotic properties, methanol has an adverse effect on the determination of very weak acids; it must therefore be present in the smallest possible proportions, and the resulting concentrated solution is diluted with benzene. It has been suggested that the methanol should be replaced by isopropanol, but tetrabutylammonium iodide is unfortunately much less soluble in the latter.

Another method of preparation consists in passing a saturated solution of the iodide in isopropanol through a column packed with a strongly basic ion exchanger in the OH form. The solution is then diluted with isopropanol. This method is not very widely used.

The stability of the solutions is satisfactory when pure materials are used. The rate of decomposition depends on the nature of the cation, the temperature, the water content, and the composition of the solvent (182). Some half-lives at elevated temperatures are given in Part III, Table IV. The decomposition products are tertiary amines, olefins, and water, i.e.,

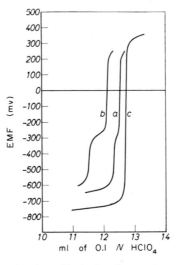

FIG. 35. Potentiometric titration of tetrabutylammonium hydroxide solution with perchloric acid in *tert*-butanol: *a*, normally prepared 0.1 *N* solution in benzene/methanol; *b*, the same solution with added carbon dioxide; *c*, solution purified by passage through an ion exchanger. [Marple and Fritz (117b).]

the normal degradation products of quaternary bases. The extent to which decomposition has occurred can be readily found by comparison of the titer of the solution with the total base content, as found by titration with aqueous hydrochloric acid and with methyl red as the indicator. The decomposition is catalyzed by amines so that solutions in pyridine are very unstable and must be stored at $-20°C$ (183). Interference due to the amine content has not been observed so far in pyridine even in the determination of strong acids (184). Such interference is not to be expected in the titration of weak acids (monocarboxylic acids and weaker), since no reaction occurs.

However, interference due to impurities has been observed in the titration of mineral acids in pyridine. This interference could be eliminated by passage of the solution through a strongly basic ion exchanger in the OH form (184). The result of the interference is that the quantity of strong acid present appears to be reduced in relation to the quantity of weak acid although the value obtained for the total acid content is correct. Thus the trouble is evidently due to the introduction of a weak acid, apparently carbon dioxide (117b) (Figs. 35 and 36).

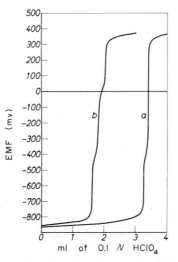

FIG. 36. Potentiometric titration of tetrabutylammonium hydroxide solutions with perchloric acid in *tert*-butanol: *a*, solution containing carbonate; *b*, solution containing carbonate as well as tertiary amine formed by decomposition. [Marple and Fritz (117b).]

After preparation, the solution must be protected against contact with atmospheric moisture and carbon dioxide. Special care should be taken to avoid impurities containing potassium or, above all, sodium ions (alkali error).

In spite of the excellent properties of the quaternary ammonium bases, it must be admitted that no ideal basic titrants have yet been found. There is at present no way of avoiding the introduction of amphiprotic solvents (methanol) into the reaction solution with the titrant solution itself, owing *inter alia* to the insolubility of the bases in pure benzene. In the titration of very weak acids, the methanol introduced makes end-point detection difficult because of protolytic reactions. To avoid the need for large quantities of titrant, therefore, the quantities of sample used should not be too large.

This also applies in the case of alkali metal solutions, which are preferred for titrations with indicators because of their ease of preparation. Isopropanol causes the least interference. The effect of added alcohol on the sharpness of the potentiometric break has been discussed by Harlow and Wyld (185).

Preparation of an 0.1 N Solution of Tetrabutylammonium Hydroxide in Methanol/Benzene (153)

Reagents:

Tetrabutylammonium iodide: Preparation: equimolar quantities of tri-*n*-butylamine and *n*-butyl iodide are refluxed on a water bath until the contents of the flask become solid. This solid is sucked dry on a filter and then washed with a little cold benzene. It is finally recrystallized once or twice from benzene. The product must be colorless, since the titer of the solution will otherwise not be constant
Methanol, anhydrous
Benzene, anhydrous
Silver oxide, finely powdered: This must be sufficiently active, and it must be free from water and alkali metal salts (remaining from the preparation of the oxide)

Tetrabutylammonium iodide (40 gm) is dissolved in 90 ml of methanol. Silver oxide (20 gm) is added, and the mixture is mechanically shaken for 1 hour. A small quantity of solution is filtered and tested for iodide; if the test is positive, 2 gm of silver oxide are added and the shaking is continued for a further 30 minutes. The iodide-free solution is filtered through a fine sintered glass filter, and the reaction vessel and the contents of the filter are washed three times with 50-ml portions of benzene. Atmospheric moisture and carbon dioxide should be excluded as far as possible. The filtrate is made up to 1 liter with benzene. The solution is protected against contact with water or carbon dioxide during storage. If a fine precipitate settles out after a time (finely divided silver iodide or silver oxide), the solution should be decanted.

For the titration of strong acids, the solution is purified as follows (184):

A column 400 mm long, with a diameter of 25 mm, and containing the strongly basic ion exchanger Amberlite IRA 400 (for analytical use) is first prepared. The ion exchanger is washed with 2 N NaOH to convert it into the hydroxide form (detected by a negative chloride test on the eluate), and the free alkali is washed out with water.

The water is removed by elution with 500 ml of absolute methanol followed by 500 ml of a 10:1 benzene/methanol mixture. The titrant solution is allowed to run through this column at a rate of from 15 to 20 ml/minute, and the eluate is collected as soon as it gives an alkaline reaction.

Another procedure (117b) involves treatment of the solution of the hydroxide (prepared from the iodide and silver oxide) in aqueous methanol with active charcoal, followed by removal of the methanol *in vacuo*. The aqueous solution is shaken with benzene to remove tertiary bases formed by decomposition, passed through an ion-exchange column, and evaporated down *in vacuo* (7 to 10 mm Hg) to a concentration of 2 *M*. The resulting crystalline hydrate is dissolved in a mixture containing 20% of isopropanol and 80% of benzene. The remaining water causes no significant interference in the titration. It can be easily removed by azeotropic distillation with isopropanol/benzene, but this leads to instability of the solution (117b).

Since concentrated aqueous solutions of the hydroxide are commercially available,* the following will probably be the most commonly used method in future. Commercial 40% tributylmethylammonium hydroxide solution (10 ml), which is known to be particularly stable (182), is dissolved in about 200 ml of a 20% solution of *tert*-butanol in benzene; roughly three-quarters of the solvent are distilled off *in vacuo* (the water present distills over as the azeotrope), and the residue is made up to 200 ml with benzene. The resulting solution, which has a concentration of approximately 0.1 *N*, is stable for several weeks (185a). Since *tert*-butanol does not interfere in the titration, it may be used as the only solvent. It may contain carbonate, but this can be removed by ion exchange (see Section III,2). The solution is stable for at least 2 months (185a).

*For example, Fluka A. G., Buchs, Switzerland; Southwestern Analytical Chemicals, Austin, Texas.

*Preparation of an 0.2 N Solution of Tetrabutylammonium Hydroxide
in Isopropanol by an Ion-Exchange Method (186)*

Reagents:

Tetrabutylammonium iodide (for preparation, see Section III,2)
Isopropanol, anhydrous

Preparation of the column: The column should have an effective
length of 52 cm and a diameter of 4.5 cm. It is packed with the strongly basic ion exchanger Amberlite IRA 400, which is washed with
1 N KOH (approximately 6 liters) to convert it into the hydroxide
form. The column is washed with water (approximately 6 liters) to
remove alkali, and then with isopropanol (approximately 5 liters) to
remove water. A saturated solution of tetrabutylammonium iodide
(400 ml) in isopropanol is slowly introduced into the column eluted at
a rate of not more than 5 ml/minute, and washed through with isopropanol. The eluate is collected as soon as it becomes alkaline. The
result is about 1 liter of a solution containing practically no iodide,
and having a concentration of approximately 0.3 N. This solution is
brought to the desired concentration by dilution with isopropanol.

Other methods for the preparation of quaternary ammonium bases:

Equally good results are obtained when triethylbutylammonium
iodide is used instead of tetrabutylammonium iodide (187). If contamination with K^+ ions does not cause interference (particularly
when indicators are used), tetraalkylammonium bases can be easily
and quickly prepared by double decomposition of tetraalkylammonium chloride and potassium isopropoxide in isopropanol, the
sparingly soluble potassium chloride being removed by filtration
(188). The solution still contains about 200 ppm of potassium.

*Preparation of an 0.1 N Solution of Potassium Methoxide in
Methanol/Benzene (189)*

Reagents:

Benzene, anhydrous
Methanol, anhydrous
Potassium

Potassium from which the outer skin has been removed is cut into
small pieces, and about 4 gm are dissolved in a mixture consisting
of 20 ml of methanol and 50 ml of benzene. The vessel is covered

with a watch glass during this operation. When the reaction is complete, the mixture is dissolved in 55 ml of methanol and made up to 1 liter with benzene. If the solution becomes turbid in the course of the addition (which must be carried out with efficient stirring), more methanol must be added until the turbidity disappears. This method gives a reagent with the lowest possible methanol content. The solution is kept in a hard glass bottle, and must be protected against contact with CO_2 and water vapor.

Standard base solutions are best standardized against benzoic acid, which is obtainable in a pure state.

PART II

Practice

CHAPTER 5

SPECIAL NOTES AND ANALYTICAL PROCEDURE

I. Determination of Bases, General

Whereas the determination of aliphatic amines presents no difficulty, satisfactory acidimetric titrations were impossible for a long time because the basicity of water and of the lower alcohols is too high. Consequently, the potentiometric determination of such compounds with perchloric acid in glacial acetic acid (126, 127, 129, 190, 191) represented a great advance, and opened up a whole new field of titration techniques in general. The electrode system used in this work consisted of a chloranil electrode and a calomel electrode. The absolute potentials were found to be surprisingly reproducible (Fig. 37).

An indicator method known as "aminometry" was proposed in 1935; this involved titration in benzene or chloroform with hydrogen chloride, dimethyl yellow being used as the indicator (192). Toluenesulfonic acid in chloroform was also used as a titrant (193, 194).

Crystal violet and α-naphtholbenzein became established as indicators for titrations in glacial acetic acid (195).

Although aprotic solvents had already been used by a number of workers, Fritz (170) was the first to realize that bases of various strengths can be titrated separately in these solvents with perchloric acid in dioxane (196). These methods subsequently underwent considerable further development.

Since even small quantities of water cause interference in the titration of very weak bases, acetic anhydride was used, first as an additive to the solvent (149) and later as the only solvent (197). This permitted the potentiometric titration of bases with pK_B values of up to about 15, which is still the upper limit.

Selective methods for the determination of certain groups had been developed even earlier. Blumrich and Bandel used the addition of acetic anhydride for the determination of tertiary amines (198), while Pifer and Wollish added mercuric acetate in the determination of hydrohalides (134). Many methods of this type are known and will be discussed in the following sections.

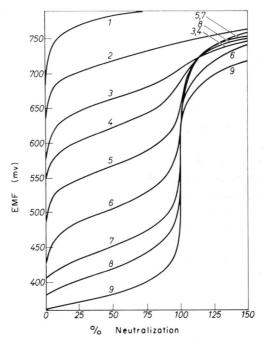

FIG. 37. Potentiometric titration of very strong bases in glacial acetic acid with perchloric acid; chloranil and calomel electrodes: 1, solvent; 2, acetanilide; 3, acetamide; 4, urea; 5, acetoxine; 6, o-chloroaniline; 7, m-chloroaniline; 8, sodium acetate; 9, guanidine. [Hall and Werner (190).]

The position can be summarized by saying that the titration of bases in organic solvents with perchloric acid has become a largely standardized routine method, the development of which now appears to have come to a standstill.

However, while this is essentially true in practice, it does not apply to theory. Following a long period in which wrong, or at least incompletely developed, ideas had prevailed with regard to the titration of bases in glacial acetic acid, Kolthoff and Bruckenstein (113, 199, 200) were the first to produce an accurate description of the processes (see also Chapter

1, Section VI). Even now, however, there is still much to learn about systems in other solvents.

Since the number of individual procedures available is enormous, we shall give here only general procedures, arranged essentially according to the basicities (pK_B values) of the bases to be determined. With the aid of the table of known pK_B values (Part III, Table I), it is generally possible to obtain a very reliable assessment of the titration methods available for a given substance (cf. also Chapter 1, Section VI).

II. Determination of Total Base

1. DETERMINATION OF BASES UP TO A pK_B VALUE OF ABOUT 12

In the determination of total base, advantage can be taken of the leveling action of glacial acetic acid, which largely cancels out any difference in basicity between the various components. This method can be used for most aliphatic and aromatic amines, nearly all of which have pK_B values of less than 12 (measured in water). Many heterocyclic bases also belong to this group. An inert solvent is often added to make the end point sharper. This can cause trouble, however, since it favors the precipitation of sparingly soluble perchlorates. Moreover, if too much of the inert solvent is added, the resulting decrease in the polarity of the solvent may interfere with the potentiometric end-point detection. With small quantities of sample and dilute solutions, up to 75% may be added, whereas with large quantities of sample, no inert solvent is required. The usual additive is dioxane, but chloroform and chlorobenzene are also used. Note that the standardization of the perchloric acid should be carried out by the same method as is used in the actual titration. When indicators are used, the tint at the end point may differ slightly from one substance to another (166).

When very weak bases (e.g., urea) are present, the indicator end point is not very sharp, and the results tend to be rather high. However, it may be possible in such cases to carry out the determination potentiometrically.

If reasonable care is used, the relative error is about ±0.2% (201, 202). The results obtained with indicators are no less accurate than those obtained by potentiometry, provided that the correct color hue is used as the end point. Otherwise a small systematic error must be expected, but this is of little importance in macrodeterminations.

Although the solvent power of acetic acid is quite satisfactory in most cases, it may be inadequate for strongly polar substances. According to

Palit (146), it may be advantageous in such circumstances to use a solvent containing glycol. The substance is first dissolved in glycol, and the solution is then diluted to twice its volume with isopropanol. Instead of hydrochloric acid in glycol/isopropanol, as recommended by Palit, this titration can also be carried out with perchloric acid in dioxane (provided that the quantity of titrant required is not too large). Since glycol is more strongly basic than glacial acetic acid, the potentiometric breaks obtained for weak bases are poorer. Thymol blue, dimethyl yellow, and methyl red may be used as color indicators in this system. The color changes of these indicators are more easily recognized, but are not sharper, than that of crystal violet in acetic acid, particularly for inexperienced observers. For example, melamine has been determined with 0.1 N perchloric acid in a 1:1 glycol/methyl glycol mixture with dimethyl yellow and thymol blue as indicators (203). This determination, unlike that in glacial acetic acid, with crystal violet as the indicator, is not affected by the presence of small quantities of urea.

The use of G-H mixtures is especially recommended for the titration of alkali metal salts (e.g., soaps). It has been found for a large number of salts of carboxylic acids that very good end points are obtained and that the solubilities of the salts are excellent (146). For the titration procedure and other methods for the determination of salts, see Chapter 5, Section IV,1,a, b.

Potentiometric Determinations

Reagents and Apparatus:
  0.1 N perchloric acid in dioxane or glacial acetic acid
  Glacial acetic acid
  Dioxane
  Chloroform
  Chlorobenzene
  Glass and calomel electrodes
  Measuring instrument or recorder

Procedure: Approximately 3.5 meq of the amine to be determined are dissolved in from 30 to 50 ml of glacial acetic acid, with heating if necessary. The potentiometric titration is then carried out in the usual manner.

This procedure was used by Markunas and Riddick (204) for the determination of several hundred compounds. The size of the sample seems rather high for many purposes, and much smaller quantities can be used with very little loss of accuracy. A better titrant in this case, however, is perchloric acid in dioxane. The sharpness of the end point is also increased, as was mentioned earlier, if dioxane is added to the titration solution (cf. Fig. 27). For microdeterminations, see Chapter 5, Section IX,1.

Determinations with Indicators

Reagents:
0.1 N perchloric acid in dioxane or glacial acetic acid
Glacial acetic acid
Dioxane
Chloroform
Chlorobenzene
Crystal violet, 0.1% in glacial acetic acid
Color comparison solutions, if required (see Chapter 4, Section II,2,a,α)

Procedure: The solution is prepared as for the potentiometric determination. In this case, the color change is much more easily recognized if an aprotic solvent is added. Three drops of the indicator solution are added, and the solution is titrated to a pure blue, i.e., until the violet tint disappears completely. Many less strongly basic amines must be titrated to a blue-green tint (see p. 88) and it is preferable in these cases to use the potentiometric method.

2. DETERMINATION OF BASES UP TO A pK_B VALUE OF ABOUT 15

Many methods have been described, together with possible sources of error and attainable accuracies, for the determination of bases with pK_B values of up to about 12. On the other hand, there are relatively few publications on compounds with pK_B values greater than 12. This range is still relatively new, and no standard methods have as yet been developed. A feature common to nearly all the methods, however, is the use of acetic anhydride as at least a component of the solvent. Pure nitromethane may also be used (150, 205). The titrant in this case is perchloric acid in nitromethane. Nitromethane has certain advantages, particularly with mixtures, owing to its inert nature; in the determination of very weak bases, however, the potentiometric break is much less sharp than in pure acetic anhydride. Other solvents that can be used include anhydrous formic acid (206) and trifluoroacetic acid (207). However, neither of these is very widely used, probably because they are expensive and difficult to obtain.

The principal classes of compounds that can be determined by this method are carbonamides, ureas, heterocyclic bases (e.g., caffeine), amine oxides (208), sulfoxides (209), phosphine oxides (208), and phosphines (205). The method can also be used for the direct determination of a number of salts of strong mineral acids, such as the halohydric acids, nitric acid (121), and sulfuric acid (up to the bisulfate stage) (Figs. 38, 39, and 40).

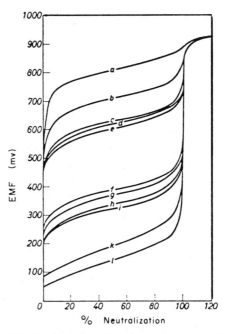

FIG. 38. Potentiometric titration of various bases in acetic anhydride with 0.05 N perchloric acid; glass and calomel electrodes: *a,* acetanilide; *b,* acetamide; *c,* caffeine; *d,* urea; *e,* methylurea; *f, N,N*-dimethylaniline; *g,* quinoline; *h,* pyridine; *i, N,N*-diethylaniline; *k, N,N*-dimethylbenzylamine; *l,* tri-*n*-butylamine. [Streuli (121).]

The acetylating action of acetic anhydride gives rise to interference with some compounds. Gremillion (197) showed, however, that urea can be quantitatively titrated at 0°C. This procedure can also be used for many amines, such as diphenylamine (168, 197), *o*-toluidine, and glycine (197). Carbonamides can be determined at room temperature (165). However, acetylation does not always cause interference since, under the conditions used, the acetylation products of (relatively) strong bases are still sufficiently basic to permit their determination (165). Neverthe-

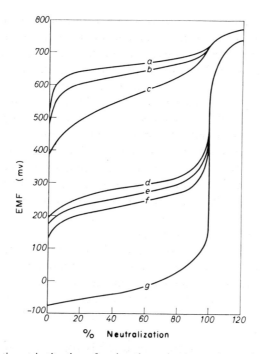

FIG. 39. Potentiometric titration of various bases in nitromethane with perchloric acid; glass and calomel electrodes: *a*, diphenylamine; *b*, *N*-methylacetanilide; *c*, urea; *d*, *N*-ethyl-*N*-methylaniline; *e*, pyridine; *f*, *N,N*-diethylaniline; *g*, *N,N'*-diphenylguanidine. [Streuli (150).]

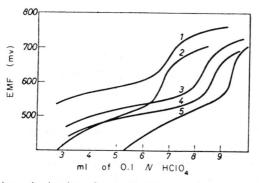

FIG. 40. Potentiometric titration of very weak bases in acetic anhydride with 0.1 *N* perchloric acid in glacial acetic acid; glass and modified calomel electrodes: 1, tetramethyl-urea; 2, *N,N*-dimethylformamide; 3, acetamide; 4, *N,N*-diethylacetoacetamide; 5, *n*-dodecylamide. [Wimer (165).]

less, in the titration of substances whose behavior is unknown, a check should always be made to find whether the method can in fact be used. The solutions in acetic anhydride should be titrated immediately after preparation, and should not be allowed to stand. Since free perchloric acid acts as an acetylation catalyst, the titration should not be carried out too quickly, particularly near the end point, and the reaction solution should be stirred well. The influence of other acetylation catalysts (e.g., pyridine) that could be introduced with the test substance has not been studied so far, but should be borne in mind if interference is encountered.

The end point is best determined potentiometrically, preferably with the aid of a recording instrument. An ordinary glass-calomel measuring cell may be used (149), but it is more strictly correct to use a modified reference electrode in which the water is replaced by acetic anhydride (165) (see Chapter 3, Section V,2,a).

The determination may also be carried out with indicators. However, a test should first be made (preferably by a potentiometric check) to ensure that the indicator in question is suitable. A special case of the use of indicators is where the color change is detected by spectrometry. This is a rather laborious method, but it is more accurate (210) (see Chapter 2, Section VII).

The leveling action of acetic anhydride is somewhat less pronounced than that of glacial acetic acid. Aliphatic and aromatic bases are almost separated in the titration curve, but the separation is not sufficiently sharp (see Chapter 5, Section III,3).

Potentiometric Determinations

Reagents and Apparatus:
   Acetic anhydride
   0.1 or 0.05 N perchloric acid and glacial acetic acid (absolutely dry)
   Glass and calomel electrodes (possibly with acetic anhydride in place
      of water in the reference electrode)
   Measuring instrument or recorder

Procedure (165): 0.5 to 1 meq of the base is dissolved in about 75 ml of acetic anhydride. Compounds that can be acetylated, such as urea, are dissolved at 0°C (197). If the substance does not dissolve readily in acetic anhydride, it may be dissolved first in a little nitromethane or glacial acetic acid. It is also permissible to use 1 or 2 ml of water to dissolve salts. The resulting solution is then diluted with acetic anhydride, and the titration and end-point detection are carried out in the usual manner. In the analysis of compounds that can be acetylated, the determination should be carried out as quickly as possible.

Modification: Perchloric acid in acetic anhydride (121) may be used instead of perchloric acid in glacial acetic acid. It has also been recommended that the pure anhydride should be replaced by a 4:1 mixture of nitromethane and acetic anhydride (149). However, this gives poorer results in the case of very weak bases.

Determinations with Indicators

Reagents:
  Acetic anhydride
  Nitromethane
  0.1 *N* perchloric acid in glacial acetic acid (absolutely dry)
  Triphenylcarbinol (0.1% solution in glacial acetic acid)
  Neutral red (0.1% solution in glacial acetic acid)
  Dibenzalacetone (0.1% solution in glacial acetic acid)

Procedure (149, 168): The solution is prepared as for the potentiometric determination. The indicator is added, and the solution is titrated to the color change. A check should be carried out in every case to ensure that the indicator selected is suitable (cf. Fig. 41).

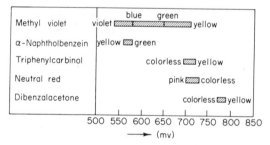

FIG. 41. Color changes of various indicators in acidimetric titrations with perchloric acid in nitromethane/acetic anhydride (4:1), as a function of the measured potential; glass and calomel electrodes. [Fritz and Fulda (149).]

III. Analysis of Mixtures of Bases

1. DETERMINATION OF COMPOUNDS WITH DIFFERENT BASICITIES IN THE PRESENCE OF ONE ANOTHER

If the common amines are arranged according to their basicities, it is possible to recognize two groups within which the individual basicities differ very little from one another. The first group, the (relatively) strong bases, consists mainly of aliphatic amines, i.e., compounds in which the free electron pair on the nitrogen is not affected by neighboring electron-attracting groups. The pK_B values of these amines are of the order of 4 ± 1.

The second group includes most of the aromatic amines. The pK_B differences within this group are considerably greater, and depend on the number and nature of substituents on the aromatic ring. The pK_B values range from about 9 to more than 12, i.e., to a region in which determinations can no longer be carried out unless special measures are taken. A number of heterocyclic bases, such as pyridine and quinoline, can also be regarded as belonging to this group.

The pK difference between the two groups, i.e., about 4 units, is quite sufficient to permit the stepwise titration of the components in the presence of one another. It is therefore often possible to determine the total aliphatic amine and the total aromatic amine in the same solution (Fig. 42).

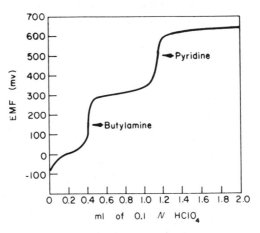

FIG. 42. Potentiometric titration of a butylamine/pyridine mixture in acetonitrile with 0.1 N perchloric acid in dioxane; glass and calomel electrodes. [Fritz (170).]

A similar situation is found in the case of the diamines. The pK difference between the two amino groups in this case is due to electrostatic effects within the molecule; it is strongly dependent on the distance between the two groups, and is only slightly affected by the polarity of the solvent (see Chapter 1, Section IV). α-Diamines can be satisfactorily titrated in steps, but this is no longer possible, e.g., in the case of hexamethylenediamine (158). This offers a simple indirect method of finding the mutual positions of amino groups. Examples of the stepwise titration of diamines are the determinations of disubstituted piperazines (211) and of disubstituted p-phenylenediamines (212) (Figs. 43 and 44).

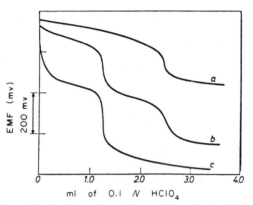

FIG. 43. Potentiometric titration of equal quantities of N,N'-bis-(1-methylheptyl)-p-phenylenediamine with perchloric acid in various solvents: a, glacial acetic acid (leveling); b, acetonitrile; c, acetone (2nd stage not detected, owing to the high basicity of acetone). [Lorenz and Parks (212).]

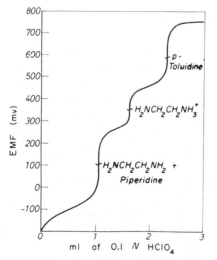

FIG. 44. Potentiometric titration of a mixture of ethylenediamine, piperidine, and p-toluidine in nitrobenzene with 0.1 N perchloric acid in dioxane; glass and calomel electrodes.

It is essential in determinations of this type to use a nonleveling solvent with a sufficiently low basicity. For this reason amphiprotic solvents, with the exception of glycol, cannot be used and determinations are nearly always carried out in aprotic solvents such as acetonitrile, nitromethane, and acetone. No more than a small percentage of glacial acetic acid can be tolerated and for this reason perchloric acid in dioxane must be used as the titrant.

The end point is nearly always detected potentiometrically, preferably with the aid of a recording instrument. The use of indicators has been described (170), but this is possible only where it has been satisfactorily established that indicators can be used; the indicator system used is eosin/crystal violet. Conductometric and spectrophotometric methods of end-point detection, while quite suitable in principle, generally give rise to complex situations in practice, and should therefore be used only for accurately known systems (see Chapter 2, Sections II and VII; Chapter 5, Section IX,3 and IX,6).

Under favorable conditions, it is even possible to detect differences among the aromatic amines themselves. For example, pyridine and caffeine (170) can be determined separately in the presence of one another. Since the sharpness of the end point in the determination of very weak bases (caffeine) is affected even by small quantities of water, it is better in this case to use perfectly anhydrous perchloric acid in glacial acetic acid as the titrant. The leveling effect of glacial acetic acid no longer operates in the very weakly basic range, since no acetates are formed with such bases (Fig. 45).

In the simultaneous determination of amines having different basicities, the samples used are generally small (semimicro quantities). This procedure leads to a slight decrease in accuracy, but is probably used in the interests of reproducibility. When the titrant solution is introduced, the composition of the titration solution changes in a manner that depends on the size of the sample used; either dioxane and water or glacial acetic acid is added with the titrant, and these can affect the potentiometric breaks.

In view of the constantly changing conditions, it is hardly necessary to adhere rigidly to a standard procedure. Moreover, the range from which the solvent can be chosen is theoretically very wide. The methods described are therefore intended only as a guide to the procedure to be used in titrations of this type.

The applicability of the method for a given pair of substances can be

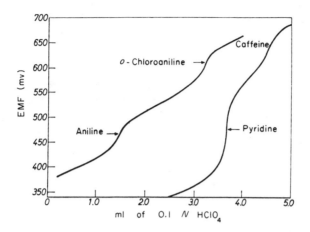

FIG. 45. Potentiometric titration of weak bases in the presence of one another in acetonitrile, with perchloric acid in glacial acetic acid (anhydrous); glass and calomel electrodes. [Fritz (170).]

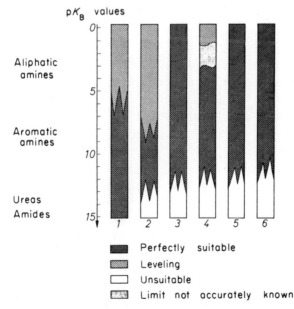

FIG. 46. Applicability of various solvents in the acidimetric titration of bases having different strengths (schematic). The pK_B values indicated relate to aqueous solutions, and should be regarded only as a guide. 1, acetic anhydride; 2, glacial acetic acid; 3, acetonitrile; 4, nitromethane; 5, nitrobenzene; 6, acetone.

satisfactorily assessed from the pK values of the substances in water. The basicities of the various compounds were found, by Fritz in the case of acetonitrile (170) and by Streuli in the case of nitromethane (150), to exhibit very good proportionality, which is independent of the solvent (see Chapter 1, Section IV). If the basicity of a compound is not known from the literature, it can be estimated by analogy. In order to obtain the best possible results, several solvents should be examined. The pK ranges in which the various solvents can be used are shown in Fig. 46.

Potentiometric Determination of Mixtures of Amines Having Different Basicities, pK_B *values* <12

Reagents and Apparatus:

Possible solvents include:
   Acetonitrile
   Acetone (or other ketones)
   Nitromethane (or nitroethane)
   Nitrobenzene

The following substances may be added to the solvent:
   Dioxane (or other ethers)
   Hydrocarbons, chloroform
   Glycol* (cannot be used for very weak bases)
   Glacial acetic acid* (in the presence of aliphatic amines, not more than
       about 5%)
   0.1 N perchloric acid in dioxane
   Glass and calomel electrodes
   Measuring instrument or recorder

Procedure: A sample containing a total of from 0.5 to 1 meq of basic nitrogen is dissolved in from 20 to 50 ml of acetonitrile.† The titration is carried out in the usual manner. A little crystal violet may be added as a check; the color change shows when the titration is complete, so that, in the absence of aliphatic amines, the titration is not carried too far beyond the first potentiometric break.

The blank titer of the solvent should be determined separately, if necessary.

If the pK_B values of the components of the mixture are known, the assignment of the potentiometric breaks is generally easy. The first

*These solvents are required in certain cases to dissolve the sample.
†Or another solvent or mixture of solvents.

break corresponds to the aliphatic amines and the second break to aromatic amines. In doubtful cases, the results are compared with those obtained for suitable test substances under identical conditions.

Potentiometric Determination of Mixtures of Amines with
pK_B *Values of from 8 to 13 (170)*

Reagents and Apparatus:
  Acetonitrile
  0.1 N perchloric acid in glacial acetic acid (anhydrous, free from acetic
    anhydride)
  Glass and calomel electrodes
  Measuring instrument or recorder

0.5 to 1 meq of the mixture of bases is dissolved in 20 ml of acetonitrile and titrated with perchloric acid in the usual manner. In the determination of a particularly weak base, when acetylation cannot take place, the sharpness of the end point can be increased by the addition of 5% of acetic anhydride.

Determination of Mixtures of Amines Having pK_B *Values* <12 *with the Aid of Indicators (170)*

Reagents:
  Acetonitrile
  Crystal violet (saturated solution in chlorobenzene)
  Eosin (saturated solution in acetonitrile)
  0.1 N perchloric acid in dioxane

0.5 to 1 meq of the mixture of bases is dissolved in 20 ml of acetonitrile. Six drops of eosin solution are added, and the solution is titrated until the color changes to pale yellow. Crystal violet is then added, and the titration is continued until a blue-green tint is obtained. The first color change corresponds to aliphatic amines, and the second to aromatic amines.

The blank titer (if any) of the solvent should be determined in the same way and subtracted from the results of the titrations.

2. DETERMINATION OF TERTIARY AMINES

The method used is based on the fact that acetyl derivatives of amines have very much lower basicities than the amines themselves. Since they have pK_B values of about 15, these derivatives can no longer be determined under normal conditions. Only primary and secondary amines can be acetylated with acetic anhydride, so that the tertiary amines can be estimated by determination of the residual basicity after reaction with acetic anhydride (213, 214).

The acetylation generally proceeds smoothly when the sample is dissolved in a glacial acetic acid/acetic anhydride mixture and allowed to stand for 15 to 30 minutes at room temperature. Aniline and many of its derivatives react instantaneously. In the case of sterically hindered secondary amines, on the other hand, it is recommended that the mixture should be refluxed for 1 hour (202). The end point is detected potentiometrically.

If only small quantities of tertiary amines are to be determined in mixtures with other amines, difficulties arise because of the need to use large samples. The large quantities of amides formed in the acetylation step flatten the potentiometric break, owing to their buffering action. For this reason, Ruch and Critchfield (148) used a mixture of acetic anhydride and methyl glycol as the solvent. Owing to the high basicity of methyl glycol in comparison with glacial acetic acid, the amides do not affect the potential curve in this solvent. On the other hand, the basicity is still sufficiently low to permit the titration of weak bases with pK_B values of up to about 10. It is interesting to note that the acetic anhydride does not react with the methyl glycol.

For the determination of tertiary amines in the form of their hydrochlorides, see Gyenes (215). In this case, mercuric acetate is added after the acetylation. Thus this is a combination of the above method with that described in Chapter 5, Section IV,1,b.

Potentiometric Determination of Tertiary Amines (214)
(Minimum Content Approximately 5% of Total Amine)

Reagents and Apparatus:
   Acetic anhydride
   Glacial acetic acid
   0.1 N perchloric acid in glacial acetic acid or dioxane
   Glass and calomel electrodes
   Measuring instrument or recorder

Procedure: A maximum of 2 gm of substance, which must not contain more than 1 gm of water, is dissolved in a mixture of 20 ml of acetic anhydride and 2 ml of glacial acetic acid. When the content of tertiary amine is high, a smaller sample is used. The solution is allowed to stand for 30 minutes at room temperature. If the sample contains secondary amines that are difficult to acetylate, the solution is refluxed for 1 hour. After the acetylation step, the solution is diluted with 30 ml of glacial acetic acid, and the potentiometric titration is carried out in the usual manner.

Determination of Small Quantities of Tertiary Amines in Mixtures with Primary and Secondary Amines (148)

Reagents and Apparatus:

Methyl glycol

Acetic anhydride

0.01 N perchloric acid in methyl glycol (0.9 ml of 72% perchloric acid dissolved in 1 liter of methyl glycol and standardized against sodium hydroxide solution

Thymol blue (0.3% in dimethylformamide)

Dimethyl yellow (0.1% in methanol)

Congo red (0.1% in methanol)

Glass and calomel electrodes

Measuring instrument or recorder

A maximum of 7 gm of the sample, which should contain not more than 0.5 meq of tertiary amines, is dissolved in 100 ml of methyl glycol. 20 ml of acetic anhydride are added, and the mixture is stirred well and allowed to stand for 30 minutes at room temperature. The solution is then titrated with 0.01 N perchloric acid, the end point being determined potentiometrically or with the aid of indicators. The correct indicator must be found by means of tests. As a rough guide thymol blue can be used for aliphatic bases (pK 4 to 7), dimethyl yellow for aromatic bases (pK 8 to 9), and Congo red for particularly weak bases of this class (pK 10). For still weaker bases, titration is no longer possible, even by potentiometric methods.

A blank titration must be carried out by the same method and subtracted from the result.

Notes: The acetylation time has only been determined for a few amines, and 30 minutes was found to be sufficient in these cases. However, this time may be too short in the case of other compounds. If heating is required, this must naturally not be carried out in the presence of methyl glycol.

Pyridine gives a poor end point in this method, probably owing to formation of an addition product with the acetic anhydride; 0.1 N acid must therefore be used for this base.

Triethanolamine must not remain in an acetylating medium for longer than 30 minutes, since interference is otherwise encountered owing to acetylation of the hydroxyl groups. The resulting O-acetate has a lower basicity, and so gives a poor end point.

3. DETERMINATION OF TERTIARY AMINES HAVING DIFFERENT BASICITIES IN THE PRESENCE OF ONE ANOTHER

The selective determination of tertiary amines depends on the use of acetic anhydride to eliminate the primary and secondary amines. The principal problem in the present determination is therefore to suppress the leveling action of the pure anhydride. This action is fortunately less pronounced than that of glacial acetic acid. Thus even in the pure anhydride, it is possible to differentiate between aliphatic and aromatic bases; however, this differentiation is still too weak to permit a determination. Nevertheless, a very satisfactory differentiation is obtained if the acetic anhydride is diluted with four times its volume of dioxane (215a). The quantity of dioxane used should, in principle, be as large as possible, but it is limited in practice by the efficiency of the measuring instrument. However, the conductivity of the 1:4 mixture is sufficiently high to permit the use of normal methods.

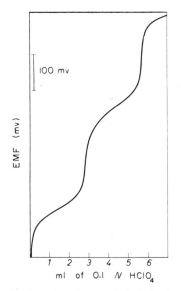

FIG. 47. Potentiometric titration of a mixture of triethylamine and dimethylaniline. Solvent acetic anhydride/dioxane 1:3; titrant 0.1 N perchloric acid in dioxane; glass and calomel electrodes.

The presence of large quantities of acetylatable amines should theoretically cause interference, but the addition of 10 parts of cyclohexylamine per 1 part of tertiary amine had no noticeable effect.

Very weak bases, such as sulfoxides and amides, can be satisfactorily determined in the presence of aromatic bases in pure acetic anhydride (216).

Reagents and Apparatus:
  Acetic anhydride, >99%
  Dioxane, anhydrous
  0.1 N perchloric acid in dioxane
  Glass and calomel electrodes
  Measuring instrument or recorder

Approximately 1 to 1.5 meq of amine (calculated on the basis of tertiary amine) are dissolved in 20 ml of acetic anhydride and allowed to stand for 30 minutes. In the presence of compounds that are difficult to acetylate, the solution must be heated. 80 ml of dioxane are added, and the potentiometric titration is carried out in the usual manner, preferably with the aid of a recording instrument. If the measuring instrument gives an unsteady reading, the conductivity of the solution is too low. In this case the 1:4 mixture of acetic anhydride and dioxane is replaced by a 1:3 mixture.

4. DETERMINATION OF PRIMARY AMINES
  IN THE PRESENCE OF OTHER AMINES

Owing to the high reactivity of primary amines, it is possible to carry out selective determinations. The principal method used is condensation with carbonyl compounds such as salicylaldehyde (170, 214, 217–221), acetylacetone (222), or benzaldehyde (223). This reaction can be evaluated in one of several ways:

(1) using the fact that the basicity of the condensation product is lower than that of the original amine (170, 214, 217, 220);
(2) by means of the decrease in the quantity of carbonyl reagent (218, 219, 222) (see also Chapter 5, Section IX,6,a);
(3) by means of the water formed during the condensation (223);
(4) by means of the extractable copper salt of the salicylaldehyde condensation product (221).

The second method, in which the sample is made to react with an excess of salicylaldehyde (218) or acetylacetone (222), is particularly useful for small concentrations of primary amines. Large quantities of other amines do not interfere with this determination, since the excess carbonyl reagent can be determined alkalimetrically, owing to the acidity of this reagent. Neither method can be used for aromatic amines, since these react incompletely or not at all in the basic solution. The acetylacetone method (222) offers certain advantages, since it is much less subject to interference (salicylaldehyde reacts abnormally with ammonia, alkanolamines, secondary heterocyclic amines, and polyamines). However, acetylacetone is less reactive, and so requires the use of more concentrated solutions.

Alkalimetric Determination of Primary Aliphatic Amines (222)

Reagents:

  Methanol, anhydrous

  Acetylacetone (the commercial product is fractionated in a column with about ten theoretical plates, and a middle fraction corresponding to about one third of the total quantity is used)

  Pyridine, freshly distilled

  2.5 N acetylacetone in pyridine (260 ml of acetylacetone are made up to 1 liter with pyridine)

  0.5 N sodium methoxide solution in methanol/pyridine [Preparation: 163 gm of sodium methoxide are dissolved in methanol and made up to 1 liter (stock solution). 167 ml of this solution and 40 ml of methanol are made up to 1 liter with pyridine, and the solution is standardized against benzoic acid. The solution is stored in a buret fitted with soda lime tubes.]

  Thymolphthalein (0.1% in pyridine)

The acetylacetone solution (10.0 ml) is pipetted into two 250-ml Erlenmeyer flasks with ground-glass necks. The sample, which should contain between 10 and 15 meq of primary amine, is placed in one of the flasks, and both flasks are then closed and allowed to stand for 1 hour at room temperature. This reaction time is long enough for most amines. In the case of amino acids, polyamines, sterically hindered amines, and hydroxyamines, the flasks are heated to 98°C for about 1 hour. At the end of the reaction, 1 ml of indicator solution is added to each flask, and the excess of acetylacetone is back-titrated with standard alkali solution. The primary amine content is found from the difference between the two titrations.

  Interfering Factors: Any acids present give rise to quantitative interference, which can therefore be eliminated by a blank titration (if a sharp indicator end point is obtainable). The indicator end point is adversely affected by more than 10% $\approx$ 1 ml of water. Alcohols, ketones, tertiary amines, esters, and nitriles do not interfere.

For very low concentrations of primary amines, a better method is that described by Johnson and Funk (218); moreover, a special method has been developed for this case.

Since the Schiff bases formed by the condensation with carbonyl compounds are much less basic than the primary amines themselves, the latter can also be determined indirectly by acidimetric titration of the secondary and tertiary amines, which do not take part in the reaction. Siggia (217) has described a method in which a glycol-isopropanol mixture is used as the solvent. The quantity of acid required to reach the first potentiometric break in this case corresponds to the total secondary and tertiary (aliphatic or aromatic). Fritz (170) used acetonitrile as the solvent. In the titration of a mixture of butylamine and dibutylamine (after the addition of salicylaldehyde), this gave two potentiometric breaks that were suitable for evaluation. The first break corresponds to the unreacted dibutylamine, and the second to the Schiff base. Huber (220) modified this method in such a way that it could also be used for aromatic amines and for mixtures of aromatic and aliphatic amines. [A method has also been described (224) for the direct determination of Schiff bases in the presence of amines.]

For a more detailed description of the above method, see Chapter 5, Section III,6.

The procedure described by Critchfield and Johnson (219) can only be used for aliphatic amines. The method consists in condensation with salicylaldehyde, followed by titration of the mixture of bases with perchloric acid, first against bromcresol green (aliphatic secondary + tertiary amines) and then against Congo red (Schiff base). Chloroform is used as the solvent, and the determination can be carried out with one sample.

Gal'pern and Bezinger (225) have described a method in which the primary amines are made to react with phthalic anhydride under reflux. It is claimed that secondary amines do not react with this reagent.

In the absence of secondary amines, primary amines can obviously be determined directly by acetylation and determination of the quantity of acetic acid used (226). However, this method is subject to interference by alcohols.

Acidimetric Determination of Primary Amines (either Aliphatic or Aromatic) (217)

Reagents and Apparatus:

Glycol/isopropanol 1:1

1 N hydrochloric acid in glycol/isopropanol 1:1 (Preparation: 96 ml of concentrated hydrochloric acid are made up to 1 liter with the solvent. Most easily standardized with 1 N NaOH.)

Salicylaldehyde, anal. grade

Glass and calomel electrodes

Measuring instrument or recorder

Total Amine

Approximately 20 meq of the amine mixture are dissolved in 50 ml of solvent and the potentiometric titration is carried out in the usual manner with 1 N hydrochloric acid.

Secondary and Tertiary Amines

Approximately 20 meq of the amine mixture are dissolved in 50 ml of solvent, and 5 ml of salicylaldehyde are added. After a reaction time of 30 minutes at room temperature, the solution is titrated potentiometrically with 1 N hydrochloric acid.

Calculation: The difference between the two values obtained gives the content of primary amine.

Interfering Factors: Ammonia reacts only partially and irreproducibly with salicylaldehyde, as does ethanolamine. The secondary amine diethanolamine also reacts to some extent.

Moreover, many acids and bases give rise to a buffering action which interferes with the end-point detection. The method cannot be used for the determination of small primary amine contents.

5. DETERMINATION OF SECONDARY ALIPHATIC AMINES IN THE PRESENCE OF OTHER ALIPHATIC AMINES

Primary and secondary aliphatic amines can be converted into dithiocarbamic acids by reactions with carbon disulfide (227). If this is preceded by reaction of the primary amines with 2-ethylhexanal, the remaining secondary amines can be determined alkalimetrically as the dithiocarbamic acids.

6. DETERMINATION OF PRIMARY, SECONDARY, AND TERTIARY ALIPHATIC AND AROMATIC AMINES IN THE PRESENCE OF ONE ANOTHER

As was mentioned in the foregoing sections, selective determinations of amines are often based on differences in the pK_B values either of the amines themselves or of derivatives that can be obtained easily and quantitatively. A group determination is therefore possible in these cases only if the components of the sample in question have pK_B values corresponding to those of normal members of this group. This value is approximately 4 for aliphatic amines, and between 9 and 10 for aromatic amines. However, this is true only when the molecule does not contain electron-attracting groups that can interact with the electron pair on the amino nitrogen (e.g., nitroanilines, but can also occur in aliphatic amines). Anomalous pK_B values are also found for diamines. In these cases, direct group separation is impossible, since the differences in the pK_B values of the individual groups are too small; moreover, difficulties encountered in the assignment of the potentiometric breaks make the analysis of unknown mixtures impossible.

On the other hand, a glance at the table of pK_B values shows that most of the common amines fit readily into the above scheme.

The least difficulty is found with aliphatic and aromatic tertiary amines. The basicities of the amides formed are so low that difficulties due to buffering occur only at very low contents of tertiary amine (see Chapter 5, Section III,3). The determination can be carried out directly, and is therefore relatively accurate.

This is not the case with primary and secondary aliphatic and aromatic amines. If these four components are present together, they must all be determined indirectly, with the exception of the primary aromatic amines. However, even the determination of this last group is not very accurate, since it is necessary to use the difference between the second and the third potentiometric breaks obtained after the addition of salicylaldehyde. For this reason, small quantities of these components in mixtures with other amines are practically impossible to determine.

If the mixture contains only aromatic amines, the procedure can be modified slightly. The Schiff bases of the primary aromatic amines appear to be stable toward acetic anhydride (demonstrated in the cases of aniline and p-toluidine). The condensation with salicylaldehyde can therefore be followed by the addition of acetic anhydride to react with the secondary amines. The advantage of this procedure is particularly noticeable in the case of mixtures containing large proportions of secondary amines. The first potentiometric break need no longer be evaluated, and it is possible to determine the total base excluding secondary amine. The second potentiometric break then corresponds to the total primary and tertiary amine. Since the Schiff bases of primary aliphatic amines are slowly cleaved by acetic anhydride, the above procedure cannot be used when these are present.

Acidimetric Determination of Primary Amines (220)
(Aliphatic and Aromatic in the Presence of One Another)

Reagents and Apparatus:
Dioxane
Nitromethane or nitroethane (possibly acetonitrile)
Glacial acetic acid
Acetic anhydride
Salicylaldehyde
0.1 N perchloric acid in dioxane
Glass and calomel electrodes
Measuring instrument or recorder (particularly recommended)

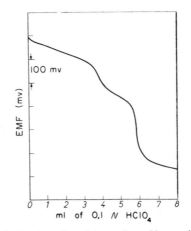

FIG. 48. Potentiometric titration of a mixture of roughly equal quantities of butylamine, dibutylamine, and trimethylamine in dioxane/glacial acetic acid/acetonitrile after addition of salicylaldehyde. First potentiometric break: dibutylamine + trimethylamine. Difference between the two breaks: butylamine (Schiff base).

Total amines (0.5 to 1.0 meq) is dissolved in 20 ml of dioxane and treated with 5 ml of glacial acetic acid and 5 ml of salicylaldehyde. The mixture is allowed to stand at room temperature for 15 minutes; 50 ml of dioxane and 20 ml of nitromethane or nitroethane are added, and the solution is titrated potentiometrically. The potential curve should be

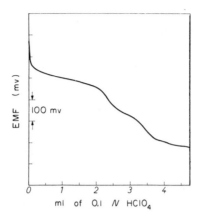

FIG. 49. Potentiometric titration of a mixture of butylamine, aniline, and pyridine in dioxane/glacial acetic acid/acetonitrile after addition of salicylaldehyde. First potentiometric break: pyridine + butylamine (Schiff base). Difference between the two breaks: aniline (Schiff base).

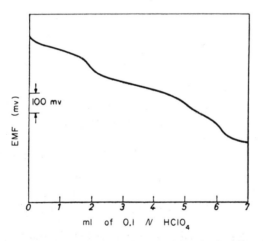

FIG. 50. Potentiometric titration of a mixture of butylamine/dibutylamine, triethylamine, aniline, methylaniline, and pyridine in dioxane/glacial acetic acid/acetonitrile after addition of salicylaldehyde. First potentiometric break: dibutylamine + triethylamine. Difference between first and second breaks: methylaniline + pyridine + butylamine (Schiff base). Difference between second and third breaks: aniline (Schiff base).

recorded. If only aromatic amines are present, 0.5 to 1.0 meq of amine is dissolved in 20 ml of glacial acetic acid. 5 ml of salicylaldehyde are added and the solution is allowed to stand for 15 minutes at room temperature. 20 ml of acetic anhydride are then added, and the mixture is allowed to stand for a further 10 minutes. 50 ml of glacial acetic acid are added, and the solution is titrated potentiometrically (Figs. 48, 49, and 50).

Evaluation: Up to three potentiometric breaks are obtained without the addition of acetic anhydride:

the first break corresponds to total secondary + tertiary aliphatic amines;

the second break corresponds to total secondary + tertiary aromatic amines + primary aliphatic amines;

the third break corresponds to primary aromatic amines.

When acetic anhydride is added (in the absence of aliphatic amines), only one potentiometric break is obtained in practice, owing to the leveling action of glacial acetic acid. This break corresponds to the total primary + tertiary amine. The content of primary amine is obtained by subtraction of the tertiary amine content, which can be determined directly.

If any difficulty is experienced in the assignment of the breaks, a qualitative test titration is carried out with a mixture of bases having similar pK_B values, and the positions of the breaks are compared with those in the principal titration. The following additional data are required for the calculation of the results:

(1) total aliphatic amine (Chapter 5, Section III,1)
(2) total aromatic amine (Chapter 5, Section III,1)
(3) total aliphatic tertiary amine (Chapter 5, Section III,3)
(4) total aromatic tertiary amine (Chapter 5, Section III,3)

Thus we have seven experimental values, from which we wish to calculate six unknowns. Two of these unknowns (the tertiary amines) are determined directly, and the others are found by difference.

IV. Special Acidimetric Determinations

1. DETERMINATION OF SALTS

a. General

In solvents with low basicities, perchloric acid is by far the strongest of all acids, since there is no leveling effect in such solvents. For this reason, many salts can be determined directly as bases in glacial acetic acid. The actual neutralization reaction is the equilibrium:

$$X^- + CH_3COOH_2^+ \leftrightarrows HX + CH_3COOH$$

$$(X^- = \text{anion of the salt})$$

which is generally displaced very strongly to the right. The only exceptions are found with the salts of very strong acids: hydrogen halides,* organic sulfonic acids, the first stage of sulfuric acid, and perchloric acid.

However, it is also essential for direct titration that the salt should be sufficiently highly dissociated. This condition is satisfied by the acetates of most monovalent and bivalent cations (see Table 4).

TABLE 4
TITRATABLE ACETATES (228)

Sodium	Manganese(II)
Potassium	Cobalt
Lithium	Nickel
Magnesium	Silver
Calcium	Lead
Strontium	Iron(III)[a]
Zinc	Chromium(III)[a]
Cadmium	Aluminum

[a]These trivalent cations apparently form complex acetates having the formula $[Me_3(OH)_2(CH_3COO)_6]$ CH_3COO, 1 mole of which consumes only 1 mole of perchloric acid. Normal calculation (3 moles of $HClO_4$/ mole of Me) from the acid consumption gives a relative content of 11.11%, which corresponds to the value obtained [for further details, see ref. (228)].

Systematic combination of the cations that can be titrated as acetates with the titratable anions (see Table V) formally gives a very large number of titratable salts. The actual number, however, is undoubtedly much smaller in practice. Many compounds are difficult to dissolve in glacial acetic acid, and this difficulty can only be partly overcome by dissolution in water and subsequent dilution with glacial acetic acid. Moreover, even the reaction with excess perchloric acid is not always possible.

The end point is best detected potentiometrically (Fig. 51). In cases in which the use of indicators is possible, a potentiometric check must be carried out to ensure that the indicator is suitable. The accuracy of the method is approximately ±0.2%. The sharpness of the end point, as

*For determination by other methods, see Chapter 5, Section IV,1,b.

TABLE 5

TITRATABLE ANIONS (AS SODIUM SALTS) (229)

Acetate[a]	Molybdate
Azide	Nitrite
Bicarbonate	Nitrate
Bisulfite	Peroxide
Borate	Primary phosphate
Bromate	Secondary phosphate
Carbonate	Tertiary phosphate
Chlorate	Silicate
Cyanide	Sulfate (1st stage)
Fluoride	Sulfide
Hydroxide	Sulfite
Hypophosphite	Thiocyanate
Iodate	Tungstate

[a] By analogy, it is assumed that the anions of practically all organic acids can be titrated.

in other titrations in glacial acetic acid, is improved by the addition of dioxane, and this addition is absolutely essential in the case of cobalt and nickel salts.

Special methods for use in special cases are available for a number of salts. The use of mercuric acetate in the determination of halides is de-

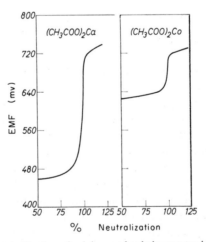

FIG. 51. Potentiometric titration of calcium and cobalt acetates in glacial acetic acid with 0.1 N perchloric acid in dioxane; glass and calomel electrodes. [Casey and Starke (228).]

scribed in Chapter 5, Section IV,1,b. If the halides are sufficiently soluble, they can also be determined directly in acetic anhydride by the method used for the determination of very weak bases. Salts of heavy metals that form stable cyanide complexes can be made so basic by the addition of acetonitrile that they become titratable (230), evidently because of the formation of a more strongly basic complex. Examples of such metals are copper, nickel, cobalt, mercury, and zinc.

Other methods are available for the titration of sparingly soluble metal salts of organic precipitants. For example, the basic nitrogen of copper oxinate (the copper salt of 8-hydroxyquinoline) can be determined by direct potentiometric titration in glacial acetic acid/acetic anhydride. Addition of acetonitrile after the potentiometric break also permits the determination of the copper acetate formed (230). Another example is the titration of nickel dimethylglyoxime. On dissolution in hot glacial acetic acid/acetic anhydride, the organic components are acetylated, and the nickel acetate formed can be determined directly after addition of acetonitrile (230).

Solvents containing glycol (G-H mixtures) offer many advantages in the determination of salts. These are much more powerful solvents than glacial acetic acid. Since they are more strongly basic, the range of substances for which they can be used is somewhat restricted. Nevertheless, they are very useful in the case of the alkali metal salts of carboxylic acids. The end point can be determined potentiometrically or with the aid of the indicator methyl red (146). Difficulties arise in the case of salts of dicarboxylic acids.

α. *Acidimetric Determination of Salts in Glacial Acetic Acid*

Reagents and Apparatus:
0.1 N perchloric acid in dioxane or glacial acetic acid
Glacial acetic acid
Glass and calomel electrodes*
Measuring instrument or recorder

The sample is finely powdered in a mortar and sifted through a 100-mesh screen (maximum particle size 0.15 mm), except in the case of readily soluble compounds. Up to 3.5 meq of the sample are dissolved in 80 ml of glacial acetic acid, with heating if necessary. If this is not

*The calomel electrode cannot be used in the case of silver and lead salts, owing to the formation of insoluble chlorides in the sintered glass diaphragm, which leads to blockage of the latter. It is necessary in these cases to use a suitable salt bridge (e.g., lithium acetate).

possible, the sample may first be dissolved in a little water (maximum 5 ml) and then diluted with glacial acetic acid. The end point is found in the usual way.

Modifications: Crystal violet may be used as an indicator in the titration of alkali metal salts of weak acids. In case of doubt, a check should be made to ensure that the indicator can be used, and to determine the exact tint at the end point.

If the salt cannot be brought into solution, perchloric acid may be added in excess and back-titrated with sodium acetate solution after reaction with the salt (see Section E,IV,2).

β. *In G-H Mixtures*

Reagents and Apparatus:
  G-H mixture (usually 1:1 glycol/isopropanol)
  0.2 *N* perchloric acid in 1:1 glycol/isopropanol (solution prepared and
     standardized as in the case of 0.1 *N* perchloric acid in dioxane
  Methyl red, 0.05% in alcohol
  Possibly dimethyl yellow or thymol blue
  Glass and calomel electrodes
  Measuring instrument or recorder

The salt (1 to 2 meq) is dissolved in 20 ml of solvent. Sparingly soluble compounds may first be dissolved in half the total quantity of glycol (with heating if necessary), the isopropanol being added afterward. When the indicator is used, 3 to 5 drops of the solution are added, and the titration is continued until a light pink tint is reached. The potentiometric determination is carried out in the usual manner.

b. *Determination of Salts of Hydrogen Halides*

Owing to the relatively high acidities of the hydrogen halides, their salts cannot be determined as such by direct acidimetric titration. However, Pifer and Wollish (134) have described a very elegant method for the determination of these salts. This method depends on the fact that mercuric acetate in glacial acetic acid has a practically negligible basicity toward perchloric acid. Since the mercuric halides, particularly in organic solvents with low polarities, are practically undissociated and so do not take part in the equilibrium, the interfering halide ions may be replaced by acetate ions by the addition of an unknown excess of mercuric acetate:

$$2 \ R_3N \cdot HX + Hg(OOCCH_3)_2 \rightarrow 2 \ R_3N \cdot HOOCCH_3 + [HgX_2]$$

$$(X = \text{halide ion})$$

The amine acetates are then titrated in the usual manner. This method can also be used for the determination of the alkali metal halides; e.g., potassium chloride can be titrated as a base, and even phosphonium halides can be determined in this way (231).

The sharpness of the end point is only slightly affected by the excess mercuric acetate. In normal determinations on the macro scale, addition of 3 gm of mercuric acetate (approximately sixfold excess) had no effect on the result. However, in microdeterminations with 0.01 N perchloric acid, the excess of mercuric acetate should not exceed 100 mole %.

Other methods for the determination of halides are by direct titration in acetic anhydride (121), where use is made of the low residual basicity of the halide ions, and by elimination of the hydrogen halide by volatilization with glacial acetic acid (232, 233). However, the mercuric acetate method is much more elegant than these.

Potentiometric Determination

Reagents and Apparatus:

0.1 N perchloric acid in dioxane

Mercuric acetate reagent (6 gm of mercuric acetate anal. grade are dissolved in 100 ml of hot glacial acetic acid. A blank titration should be carried out; the result should be practically zero in the case of a pure reagent.)

Glass and calomel electrodes

Measuring instrument or recorder

Procedure: About 3 meq of the hydrochloride are dissolved in 70 ml of glacial acetic acid, with heating if necessary. The solution is cooled, 10 ml of mercuric acetate reagent are added, and the titration is carried out in the usual manner.

If a smaller quantity of hydrochloride is used, before the perchloric acid is added, sufficient dioxane should be introduced to give a dioxane concentration of about 30% near the end point.

Determination with Indicators

Reagents:

0.1 N perchloric acid in dioxane

Crystal violet, 0.1% in glacial acetic acid

Color comparison solutions if required (see Chapter 4, Section II, 2,a,α)

Procedure: The sample is prepared as for the potentiometric determination. Indicator (3 to 5 drops) is added and the titration is continued until the solution turns blue.

2. DETERMINATION OF AMINO ACIDS

Direct titration of amino acids with perchloric acid in glacial acetic acid presents no fundamental difficulties, since the basicities of the compounds are perfectly adequate. However, a problem is raised by the fact that most amino acids have low solubilities in glacial acetic acid. Nadeau and Branchen (234) overcame this difficulty by reaction of the amino acids with perchloric acid to obtain the more readily soluble perchlorates, followed by back-titration of the excess acid with a suitable base.

This method has also been used for other classes of compounds (phenothiazines) (235), and so deserves consideration for the titration of sparingly soluble compounds. The end point was originally determined by means of an indicator, but potentiometric titration can also be used.

For the alkalimetric determination of amino acids, see Chapter 5, Section VIII,1.

Reagents:
  Glacial acetic acid
  Crystal violet, 0.1% in glacial acetic acid (methyl violet)
  0.1 *N* perchloric acid in glacial acetic acid
  0.1 *N* sodium acetate solution in glacial acetic acid, prepared by dissolution of 4.150 gm of anhydrous sodium carbonate anal. grade in glacial acetic acid, the solution then being made up to 1 liter.

Procedure: The amino acid (2 to 3 meq) is dissolved in 50.0 ml of 0.1 *N* perchloric acid. Indicator is added and the titration with sodium acetate solution is continued until the color changes to violet.

3. DETERMINATION OF SULFATE

Owing to the insolubility and consequent neutrality of barium sulfate, the sulfate ion can be determined by an indirect acidimetric method (236). A known quantity of a 0.05 *N* barium acetate solution in glacial acetic acid is added to the aqueous solution of the sample, the quantities being such that the barium acetate is present in excess. The water is taken up with excess acetic anhydride, and the excess of barium acetate is back-titrated potentiometrically with 0.05 *N* perchloric acid. This method was specially developed for nuclear reactor solutions containing uranium. The reader is referred to the original publication for more detailed procedures and information about interfering factors.

4. DETERMINATION OF NITRILES

Nitriles can be quantitatively converted into primary amines by catalytic hydrogenation in glacial acetic acid with palladium as the catalyst. The primary amines are then titrated acidimetrically with 0.1 N perchloric acid, α-naphtholbenzein being used as the indicator; 0.5 to 1.0 meq of the nitrile is used (237).

The advantage of this method (a combination of an hydrogen number with an acidimetric titration) is that any carbonamides present as impurities do not interfere with the determination, since they are not hydrogenated and so do not act as bases during the titration. (In the determination of nitriles by acid or alkaline hydrolysis, the carbonamides are also included in the result.) Normal unsaturated compounds do not interfere, since they do not form bases on hydrogenation.

5. DETERMINATION OF EPOXIDES

The ability of the grouping

to add on hydrogen halides, with ring cleavage, can be used for the determination of this group. This determination is best carried out in organic solvents, particularly where the solubility of the compound in water is low. The ring-cleavage reaction is so fast that the epoxide can be titrated as a base. A hydrogen halide must be used as the titrant, hydrobromic acid being preferred to the less strongly acidic hydrochloric acid. The end point can be determined either potentiometrically or with color indicators (238).

Reagents:

Chlorobenzene

Glacial acetic acid

0.1 N hydrogen bromide in glacial acetic acid. (Preparation by introduction of dry hydrogen bromide into glacial acetic acid, or possibly by dissolution of equimolar quantities of acetyl bromide and water in glacial acetic acid. Standardized with sodium carbonate in glacial acetic acid, with crystal violet as the indicator. Must be protected against contact with water vapor during storage.)

Glass and calomel electrodes

Measuring instrument or recorder

Procedure: 0.3 to 0.6 gm of the sample is dissolved in chlorobenzene; 5 drops of indicator are added, and the solution is titrated with acid until the color changes to blue-green. Glacial acetic acid is used as the solvent for the potentiometric titration. In this case the titration must be carried out immediately, since the substance otherwise reacts slowly with the glacial acetic acid. Atmospheric water vapor should be excluded as far as possible.

Modifications: The use of hydrogen bromide solution can be avoided by the addition of an unmeasured quantity of trimethylamine hydrochloride in glacial acetic acid (239). The epoxide reacts with the hydrogen chloride present, so liberating an equivalent quantity of the tertiary amine, which can then be back-titrated with 0.1 N perchloric acid in the presence of crystal violet. A better end point would probably be obtained by the use of a hydrobromide instead of a hydrochloride.

If the substance in question already contains bases (salts of carboxylic acids, amines), the epoxide group can still be determined selectively (240), since the hydrogen bromide added on is no longer ionogenic. A measured excess of hydrogen bromide may therefore be added and the ionogenic component back-titrated argentometrically. Alternatively, the titration may be carried out in the usual manner to the crystal violet end point, the content of ionic bromide then being found by addition of mercuric acetate followed by titration with 0.1 N perchloric acid (see Chapter 5, Section IV,1,b).

V. Determination of Acids, General

The first organic solvents to be used in the determination of acids were alcohols, particularly ethanol; these were used in the analysis of compounds that are sparingly soluble in water. The relationships are fundamentally similar to those found in water, the only essential point of difference being the solubility. As was to be expected in view of the technical position at that time, it was not recognized that alcohols also offered improved conditions for the stepwise titration of polybasic acids. The earliest papers on titrations in hydrocarbons with sodium alkoxide (241, 242) were ignored. Following the success of the titration of bases in glacial acetic acid, attempts were made to develop similar methods for the determination of weak acids. In the belief that the solvent used for the determination of very weak acids should be as strongly basic as possible, Moss *et al.* (243) used ethylenediamine for the titration of phenols.

This led to the development of methods that make routine work of relatively difficult determinations which had previously been regarded as impossible. The main credit for this development, apart from the improvement of electrometric methods of end-point detection, culminating in the production of recording instruments, is due to the introduction of new solvents and, above all, new titrants.

The strongly basic amphiprotic solvents, such as ethylenediamine and butylamine, have been gradually displaced (244, 245) by aprotic solvents. The practical advantages of these solvents are the reduction or elimination of leveling, and above all the fact that they are much more pleasant and less troublesome to use. Blank values due to atmospheric carbon dioxide are practically nonexistent in these solvents, and there is no inconvenience due to unpleasant odors, except in the case of pyridine. The titratable pH range is so wide that a mixture of five acids ranging from perchloric acid to phenol has been determined by potentiometric titration in methyl isobutyl ketone (see Chapter 4, Section I,3).

The introduction of the strongly basic quaternary ammonium hydroxides as titrants (186, 246, 247) made possible the general use of the glass electrode even in the titration of very weak acids, and so represented a decisive practical advance.

As has already been mentioned, the acids that can be titrated by modification of classic methods in this way range from the strongest acids to phenol ($pK_A = 9.9$). For the determination of still weaker acids, such as alcohols ($pK_A > 16$), it is necessary to use different titrants, since alkoxides or hydroxides are no longer sufficiently basic. This bring us to a pK range in which entirely different principles are used, very weak acids being determined through the active hydrogen by the Zerewitinoff method, in which organometallic compounds are used as the reagents. The first titrant of this type, introduced by Corwin and Ellingson (248), was triphenylmethylsodium, with which pyrroles can be determined as acids.

Higuchi *et al.* (249) used lithium aluminum hydride, the end point being determined potentiometrically as a redox process. This method suffers from the disadvantage of reductive side reactions. For this reason the hydride was later replaced by its reaction product with secondary amines, which, being a metal amide, has an extremely high basicity (250, 251). When these compounds are used, the end point is determined by means of indicators.

However none of these methods has become very widely used. Apart from susceptibility to interference by small quantities of impurities (e.g., water), this is probably due to their nonuniform reaction with many compounds. In acetamide, for example, only 1.2 to 1.3 of the two active hydrogens are detected by the titration.

As for the titration of bases, a number of general procedures are given in the following sections, arranged according to the strengths of the acids to be determined. For the pK_A values of acids, see Part Three, Table I.

VI. Determination of Total Acids

1. DETERMINATION OF ORGANIC ACIDS UP TO A pK_A VALUE OF ABOUT 7

This group consists mainly of carboxylic acids, but also includes many enols, imides, and sulfonamides. Practically no difficulties are encountered, owing to the high acidities. Many of these compounds can also be determined in aqueous solution, if their solubility is sufficiently high. The classic titration in alcoholic solution with phenolphthalein as indicator can be advantageously replaced by other methods.

Strongly basic amphiprotic solvents, such as ethylenediamine (243) and butylamine (252), should be used only in special circumstances. They have a more or less high blank titer, must be carefully protected against contact with atmospheric carbon dioxide during the titration, and have an oppressive odor. Acids stronger than carboxylic acids are leveled in these solvents, and, while this is not necessarily a disadvantage, it limits their usefulness to some extent. The leveling tendency is much less pronounced even in pyridine, only strong mineral acids being leveled in this solvent. However, exclusion of atmospheric carbon dioxide is still essential. In the case of dimethylformamide, on the other hand, the absorption of carbon dioxide is so slight that the only precaution necessary in many cases is a light cover on the titration vessel. In the determination of acids in dimethylformamide without protective measures, the error found after a stirring time of 30 minutes was only about 0.5% (253). Acetone and similar neutral solvents are even better. This applies only to normal titrations, however, and atmospheric carbon dioxide must always be carefully excluded in micro or trace determinations.

The titrants used in potentiometric titrations are generally quaternary ammonium bases, which permit the use of the glass electrode in any pH range. In titrations with indicators, however, it is preferable to use solutions of potassium methoxide in benzene/methanol which are easier to prepare. It is even possible in many cases to use simple alcoholic (especially isopropanol) potassium hydroxide solutions. If interference is encountered as a result of precipitation of potassium salts during the titration, it may be advantageous to use a quaternary ammonium base containing potassium prepared by double decomposition with potassium methoxide (see Chapter 4, Section III,2).

Potentiometric Determination of Acids

Reagents and Apparatus:
   0.1 *N* tetrabutylammonium hydroxide solution
   Isopropanol
   tert-Butanol
   Dimethylformamide
   Acetone (or other ketones)
   Acetonitrile
   Pyridine
   Ethylenediamine
   Butylamine
   Glass and calomel electrodes
   Measuring instrument or recorder

The acid (0.3 to 0.8 meq) is dissolved in about 40 ml of solvent (preferably isopropanol or acetone). The potentiometric titration is then carried out in the usual manner.

A blank titer must be found and subtracted from the values obtained in the actual titration.

Determination with Indicators

Reagents:
   0.1 *N* potassium methoxide in methanol/benzene
   Dimethylformamide
   Thymol blue (0.1% in isopropanol)
   Phenolphthalein (0.1% in isopropanol)
   Azo violet, saturated solution in benzene

Dimethylformamide (20 ml) containing some indicator solution is titrated to the color change (this normally requires only a few drops of titrant). The weighed sample of acid (0.3 to 0.8 meq) is then dissolved in the neutralized solvent and titrated to the same tint. The color changes of thymol blue and phenolphthalein occur in roughly the same range, and are suitable for the determination of acids with pK_A values of about 5. Both indicators give sharp end points. For weaker acids, such as negatively substituted phenols (but not phenol itself), azo violet is a better indicator.

Water in quantities of more than a trace can have a hydrolytic effect and lead to high results, but the extent of the interference appears to depend on the substance (254). In one case a water content of 2.5% gave rise to an error of +1% (254).

Modification: Ethylenediamine may be used instead of dimethylformamide, but the only indicator that can be used in this case is azo violet.

2. DETERMINATION OF ACIDS UP TO A pK_A VALUE OF ABOUT 11 (ESPECIALLY PHENOLS)

The best method is potentiometric titration with tetrabutylammonium hydroxide in a neutral solvent, preferably *tert*-butanol or acetone. Other solvents that can be used include methyl isobutyl ketone, dimethylformamide, ethylenediamine, butylamine, acetonitrile, and particularly pyridine. Acetone is probably the best in most cases, because of its ready availability, cheapness, and purity. However, *tert*-butanol and pyridine give sharper potentiometric breaks.

The determination can also be carried out with indicators. However, the end-point detection is not as sharp as in the titration of carboxylic acids, so that a greater error (about ±0.5%) is to be expected. Ethylenediamine and dimethylformamide can be used as solvents. Both (but dimethylformamide in particular) are sensitive to methanol introduced with the titrant solution, which interferes with the color change, and for this reason the quantity of sample used must be small. *o*-Nitroaniline is used as the indicator (or azo violet for more strongly acidic phenols, see Chapter 5, Section VI,1).

Potentiometric Determination

Reagents and Apparatus:
　　0.1 N tetrabutylammonium hydroxide solution
　　tert-Butanol
　　Acetone (or methyl isobutyl ketone)
　　Pyridine
　　Dimethylformamide
　　Glass and calomel electrodes
　　Measuring instrument or recorder

The substance (0.3 to 0.9 meq) is dissolved in 50 ml of solvent, and the potentiometric titration is carried out in the usual manner. Atmospheric carbon dioxide must be excluded when pyridine is used, and the same precaution is recommended in the cases of dimethylformamide and acetone. A blank titer must be found for the solvent.

Determination with Indicators

Reagents:
   0.1 *N* potassium methoxide solution
   Ethlenediamine
   o-Nitroaniline, 0.5% in benzene

Procedure: 25 ml of ethylenediamine containing 2 drops of indicator solution are titrated until the color changes to red. A maximum of 0.6 meq of the substance is then added, and the solution is titrated to the same tint.

Modification: Dimethylformamide may be used instead of ethylenediamine. It is particularly important in this case to observe the upper limit for the size of the sample.

3. DETERMINATION OF ACIDS UP TO A pK_A VALUE OF OVER 20 (ESPECIALLY ALCOHOLS)

The titrant used in this case is a 1 *N* solution of lithium aluminum amide in tetrahydrofuran (251). The end point is determined with the aid of indicators. With some compounds, nonstoichiometric reactions occur. Higuchi *et al.* (250, 251) report the experimental values shown in Table 6.

TABLE 6

Compound	Equivalents	Compound	Equivalents
Ethanol	1	Phthalic anhydride	2
n-Pentanol	1	Phenyl salicylate	2
α-Naphthol	1	Acetanilide	1
Acetophenone	1	Acetamide	1.2–1.3
Benzophenone	1	Carbazole	1
Benzyl benzoate	1	Phthalimide	2.2–2.5

The titration solution is slightly sensitive to air, and must therefore be kept under nitrogen.

Instead of a lithium aluminum amide solution, it is also possible to use a solution of the corresponding hydride. In this case the end point may be determined either with the same indicator (250) or potentiometrically (255) (platinum and silver electrodes). The determination is carried out in the same manner. Owing to the hydrogenating action of the hydride, however, the determination is more susceptible to interference than in the case of the amide.

Another titrant that can be used is triphenylsodium. This was used for the determination of pyrroles as acids in an ether-toluene mixture (248). No indicator is required in this case, owing to the intense red color of the reagent itself.

Determination of Alcohols

Reagents:

1. 1 *N* butanol solution. (Preparation: Pure *n*-butanol is obtained by fractionation, the early and late fractions being rejected; 74.12 gm of the pure alcohol are placed in a 1-liter graduated flask and made up to the mark with dry benzene.)

1. 1 *N* lithium aluminum amide solution. [Preparation: 25 gm of $LiAlH_4$ are refluxed for 24 hours with 1 liter of dry benzene. When the solution has cooled, the sediment is allowed to settle (or centrifuged) and the supernatant liquid is decanted into a dry flask, dry nitrogen being blown in throughout the operation. The solution is roughly standardized against 1 *N* butanol solution with *p*-phenylaminoazobenzene as the indicator. The result of this standardization can be used to find the quantity of dibutylamine or piperidine required for amide formation. A small excess of the pure amine is added (the molar ratio is 4:1), and the solution is protected from air and light during storage.]

Tetrahydrofuran, twice distilled over $LiAlH_4$ (cannot be stored for more than a few days, owing to the danger of peroxide formation)

p-Phenylaminoazobenzene, 0.1% in benzene

Procedure: The sample is weighed into an absolutely dry 125-ml Erlenmeyer flask; 15 ml of tetrahydrofuran and 5 ml of lithium aluminum amide solution are pipetted in. 5 drops of indicator solution are added and the solution is titrated with butanol until the color changes to yellow; during titration, nitrogen is passed in and the solution is stirred with a magnetic stirrer. Any water present will also be included in the titer.

The titer of the amide solution is determined under the same conditions.

VII. Analysis of Mixtures of Acids

1. Determination of Acids of Different Strengths in the Presence of One Another (Mineral Acids, Carboxylic Acids, and Phenols)

This important field of analysis has been very extensively studied. The principal methods are potentiometric methods involving the use of aprotic solvents and with quaternary ammonium bases as titrants. Five acids of different strengths (perchloric acid, hydrochloric acid, salicylic acid, acetic acid, and phenol) have been titrated in the same solution in methyl isobutyl ketone (see Chapter 4, Section I,3,f). It should be noted that salicylic acid acts as a monobasic acid in this case (see Fig. 61).

Although ketones are very useful solvents, having practically no blank titer, they suffer from the disadvantage that they react to a small extent with strong acids, so that the results are subject to an error of about 1%

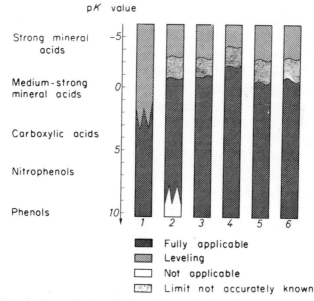

FIG. 52. Use of solvents for the alkalimetric determination of acids of different strengths (schematic). The pK_A values indicated refer to aqueous solutions, and should be regarded as a guide. 1, ethylenediamine; 2, isopropanol; 3, *tert*-butanol; 4, acetone; 5, dimethylformamide; 6, pyridine.

(256). The same is true of alcohols, acetonitrile, and above all dimethyl-formamide. As far as is known at present, pyridine appears to be the only solvent that is not restricted in this respect; however, this solvent levels the strong mineral acids, with the result that they can no longer be distinguished, although sulfuric acid can be determined as a dibasic acid in pyridine.

An even stronger leveling effect is observed with the strongly basic solvents ethylenediamine and butylamine. The ranges in which the various solvents can be used are indicated in Fig. 52.

It is probably very rare in practice for acids of such widely different strengths to be present in the same solution. Considerable difficulties also arise in accurate quantitative determinations, in connection with the blank titers of the solvents and the normality factors of the solutions. Both of these quantities depend, in theory, on the pK value of the acid to be titrated. This needs no explanation in the case of the blank titers, since acidic impurities with different pK values could quite easily be present. However, the titrant solution may also contain similar impurities, as well as carbon dioxide absorbed from the atmosphere (Fig. 36). Its normality factor will therefore depend on the acidities of the compounds to be titrated and on the relative quantities in which they are present. Both effects are particularly pronounced in the determination of weak acids.

These errors can be reduced by the following precautions:

(1) Solvents with the lowest possible blank titers (particularly ketones or *tert*-butanol) should be chosen, and a separate blank titer should be determined for each potentiometric break.

(2) The quaternary ammonium base should be specially purified by means of anion exchangers (see Chapter 4, Section III,2).

Errors may also arise if the potentiometric breaks are situated too close together (see Section B,I).

These remarks are not intended to belittle the analytical value of the titration method, since they really apply to extreme cases that are very seldom encountered in practice. In general, only two or at most three potentiometric breaks will be expected, and problems of this nature can be easily solved in most cases by a suitable choice of solvent (Figs. 53–57). It is not necessary to adhere rigidly to the solvents listed, and it may be preferable to use combinations. The addition of nonpolar solvents such as benzene may be particularly valuable in difficult cases.

The notes contained in the theoretical part of this book regarding the use of solvents should then be used as a guide.

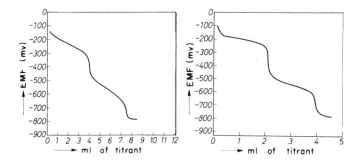

FIG. 53. Potentiometric titration of benzoic acid/phenol with 0.1 N tetrabutylammonium hydroxide solution in benzene/isopropanol. Solvents: left, acetone; right, *tert*-butanol. Glass and calomel electrodes. [Fritz and Marple (144).]

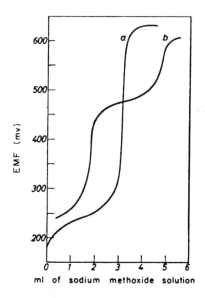

FIG. 54. Potentiometric titrations in butylamine with sodium methoxide solution; antimony and glass electrodes (cf. Chapter 3, Section V,2,c). *a*, benzoic acid; *b*, benzoic acid/ phenol. [Fritz and Lisicki (252).]

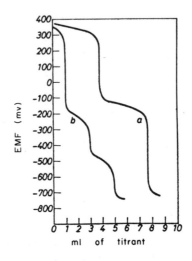

FIG. 55. Potentiometric titration of various acids in *tert*-butanol with 0.1 *N* tetrabutyl-ammonium hydroxide; glass and modified calomel electrodes: *a, p*-toluenesulfonic acid + benzoic acid; *b, p*-toluenesulfonic acid + *p*-hydroxybenzoic acid. [Fritz and Marple (144).]

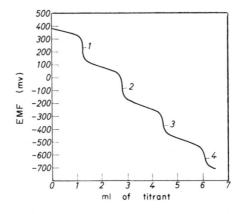

FIG. 56. Potentiometric titration of (1) picric acid, (2) 2,4-dinitrophenol, (3) *o*-nitro-phenol, and (4) phenol in the same solution in *tert*-butanol with 0.1 *N* tetrabutylammonium hydroxide; glass and calomel electrodes. [Fritz and Marple (144).]

An interesting special case of the potentiometric method involves the use of glass and silver electrodes (257). With pyridine as the solvent and sodium methoxide as the titrant, this electrode combination gives a potential curve that passes through a sharp minimum at the end point, and so formally resembles the curves obtained in voltammetry. However, this minimum is observed only with acids of about the same strength as carboxylic acids. Weaker and stronger acids (which may also be present in mixtures) give normal potentiometric breaks, except that the sign is reversed.

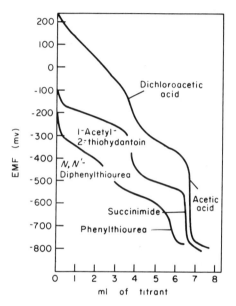

FIG. 57. Potentiometric titration of various acids in acetone with 0.1 N triethylbutyl-ammonium hydroxide; glass and calomel electrodes. [Fritz and Yamamura (187).]

Potentiometric Determination of Mixtures of Acids

Reagents and Apparatus:
0.1 N tetrabutylammonium hydroxide solution (specially purified if necessary)
tert-Butanol
Pyridine
Acetone (or methyl isobutyl ketone)
Dimethylformamide
Isopropanol (possibly diluted with benzene)
Ethylenediamine or butylamine

Glass and calomel electrodes
Measuring instrument or recorder

Approximately 0.3 to 0.9 meq of the substance is dissolved in about 50 ml of solvent, and the potentiometric titration is carried out in the usual manner. In the case of mixtures of unknown substances, the absolute potentials are best determined by a qualitative comparison titration with known substances.

Determination of Carboxylic Acids and Phenols in the Presence of One Another, with the Aid of Indicators

The total acid is first determined by the procedure described for the determination of phenols. The carboxylic acids are determined separately by the following method, and the result is subtracted from the total acid figure (Fig. 58).

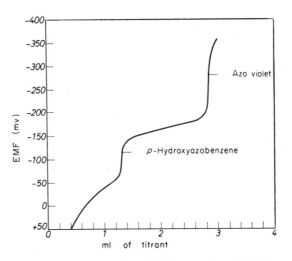

FIG. 58. Stepwise titration of mandelic acid + 2-aceto-1-naphthol in acetonitrile with 0.1 N potassium methoxide. Potentiometric check on the color changes of the indicators shown. [Fritz and Keen (245).]

Reagents:
   0.1 N potassium methoxide solution
   Acetone or acetonitrile
   p-Hydroxyazobenzene, 0.2% in benzene

Solvent (30 to 40 ml) containing 2 drops of indicator solution is neutralized (this step may be omitted if the solvent is sufficiently pure). The substance (0.5 to 1.0 meq) is weighed into the solvent and titrated to the sharp color change to yellow.

Modification: Both determinations can be carried out in succession on a single sample if dimethylformamide is used as the solvent (258). After the *p*-hydroxyazobenzene color change has occurred, *o*-nitroaniline is added and the titration is continued until the red color appears. The total size of the sample in this case should not exceed 0.5 meq.

2. STEPWISE TITRATION OF POLYBASIC ACIDS (MINERAL ACIDS, CARBOXYLIC ACIDS, AND PHENOLS)

It is often desirable to be able to titrate polybasic acids in steps, either in order to elucidate the structure of the compound or to determine the acid in question selectively in the presence of other acids. A dibasic acid H_2X dissociates in two stages:

$$H_2X = H^+ + HX^-$$

$$HX^- = H^+ + X^{2-}$$

The two acids H_2X and HX^- differ in their electric charge. The ratio of the two acidity constants $K_{A(H_2X)}$ and $K_{A(HX^-)}$ is therefore very strongly dependent on the dielectric constant of the solvent (see Chapter 1, Section IV). The lower the dielectric constant the lower will be the acidity of the negatively charged acid HX^- in relation to the uncharged H_2X. To obtain the best possible separation of the two stages, therefore, the polarity of the solvent used should be as low as possible (259, 260). In some cases, however, this effect may be masked by specific solvent effects.

The relative decrease in the acidity of the acid HX^- is due to electrostatic factors, and so depends strongly on the structure of the molecule H_2X. Consequently, a second factor that affects the separation of the two stages is the distance between the two negative charges in the ion X^{2-} (261). Inorganic polybasic acids (e.g., sulfuric acid) can be titrated in stages in organic solvents with dielectric constants of less than 40, provided that the solvent is fundamentally suitable from the point of view of leveling and protolysis.

Aliphatic dicarboxylic acids at least up to succinic acid can be satisfactorily determined in stages in isopropanol (dielectric constant 18.3) (Figs. 59 and 60).

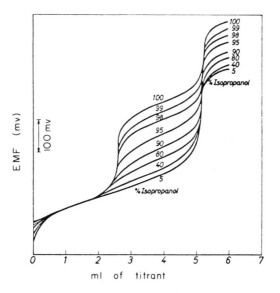

FIG. 59. Potentiometric titration of equal quantities of succinic acid in isopropanol/ water mixtures of various concentrations, with tetrabutylammonium hydroxide; glass and calomel electrodes. The curves are displaced in relation to one another in such a way as to make the first plateaus coincide. [Harlow and Wyld (259).]

Of the aromatic dicarboxylic acids, *o*-phthalic acid can be readily titrated in two stages in dimethylformamide. However, this is no longer possible in the case of terephthalic acid if the salts formed remain in solution. If, for example, potassium terephthalate precipitates, a potential curve with two jumps is obtained. However, accurate evaluation of the jumps is very difficult, since they depend on the concentration and the titration speed. Moreover, interference may occur as a result of co-precipitation. For this reason, it is preferable to use organic bases as titrants, since no precipitates are formed in these cases.

Stepwise titration of acid groups of fundamentally different acidities (e.g., in phenolcarboxylic acids) presents no difficulties when carried out in solvents with sufficiently low acidities, and does not differ appreciably from the titration of different acids in the presence of one another (Fig. 61). On the other hand, the stepwise titration of polyphenols is rather difficult. In many cases only one of the hydroxyl groups is titrated (e.g., in resorcinol) (262). However, differentiation is possible in the titration of polyhydroxyanthraquinones in ethylenediamine (263), as well as in pyridine (264) and dimethylformamide (265).

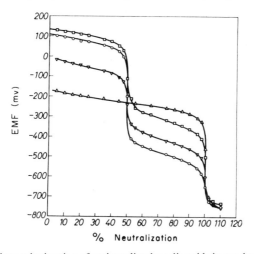

FIG. 60. Potentiometric titration of various dicarboxylic acids in *tert*-butanol with 0.15 N tetrabutylammonium hydroxide; glass and calomel electrodes: □, oxalic acid; O, malonic acid; ◁, succinic acid; △, sebacic acid. [Fritz and Marple (144).]

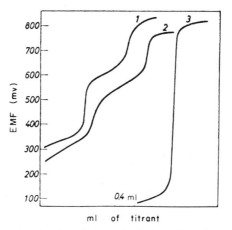

FIG. 61. Potentiometric titration of isomeric hydroxybenzoic acids with tetrabutylammonium hydroxide in pyridine: 1, *m*-hydroxybenzoic acid; 2, *p*-hydroxybenzoic acid; 3, *o*-hydroxybenzoic acid (monobasic). [Cundiff and Markunas (247).]

In the case of a dibasic acid in the presence of a monobasic acid of similar strength, two potentiometric breaks are again generally observed. The quantity of titrant required to reach the first break then corresponds to the sum of the monobasic acid and the first stage of the dibasic acid, while the quantity required to reach the second break from this point corresponds to the second stage of the dibasic acid. The quantity of monobasic acid is found from the difference between the two titers.

The situation is more complicated if the system contains two monobasic acids of different strengths, in addition to the dibasic acid. In this case several determinations are carried out in solvents with different polarities. A modification of this method consists in the addition of water to the titration solution after the first break has been reached (259) (Fig. 62).

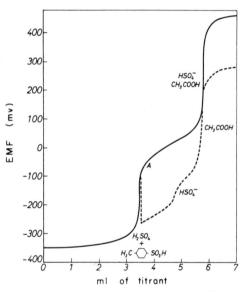

FIG. 62. Potentiometric titration of sulfuric acid, *p*-toluenesulfonic acid, and acetic acid in the presence of one another in 50 ml of isopropanol. Titrant: tetrabutylammonium hydroxide; glass and calomel electrodes. —————, normal titration; ---------, with addition of 50 ml of water at *A*.

Methods of this type are mainly of interest for the determination of sulfuric acid in mixtures with other acids, particularly mineral acids. These mixtures could, in principle, be satisfactorily analyzed by the general methods for the determination of acids having different strengths.

Owing to the high acidity of the components, however, it would be too costly to use the strongly basic tetrabutylammonium hydroxide. Alcoholic alkali solutions could theoretically be used and are readily obtainable, but the interference may occur as a result of the precipitation of sparingly soluble salts, particularly sulfates. It is best, therefore, to use an aliphatic amine with a sufficiently high basicity.

The choice of solvents and methods is wide. Critchfield and Johnson (266) used acetonitrile as the solvent and morpholine as the titrant. Das and Mukherjee (267) used G-H mixtures, whereas Stuck (268) proposed methanol as the solvent, since it can be obtained cheaply in a very pure state, and cyclohexylamine as the titrant. Special advantages of methanol as the solvent are its high solvent power for salts and the fact that it is not sensitive to small quantities of water. This is evidently because the dielectric constant of methanol is scarcely affected by a little water. Moreover, small quantities of water are not expected to have much effect on the protolytic activity of the system, since water and methanol are very similar in this respect. The method was developed for relatively large samples, since large samples greatly facilitate the analysis of mineral acids.

If the mineral acids are present as salts, the determination can be carried out by one of two procedures. In one case the salts are titrated directly in methanol solution with 1 N perchloric acid in methanol. The potentiometric breaks then occur in the reverse of the normal order, i.e., the third break occurs first (this break may therefore also include salts of acids weaker than carboxylic acid), and the second break comes next; the first break cannot occur. Thus the acids of this category cannot be determined, with the exception of sulfuric acid, which is titrated as a monobasic acid.

A second method, of less limited application, involves ion exchange in methanol solution, the salts being converted in this way into the free acids, which can then be titrated in the usual manner (see also Chapter 5, Section VIII,1).

For the selective conductometric determination of sulfate, particularly in sulfonates, see Chapter 5, Section IX,3.

Potentiometric Determination of Polybasic Acids

The reader is referred to the procedure for the titration of acids of different strengths in the presence of one another (Chapter 5, Section VII,1).

*Potentiometric Determination of Mixtures of Acids
Including Strong Mineral Acids (268)*

Reagents and Apparatus:

Methanol

1 N cyclohexylamine solution in methanol. [Preparation: 100 gm of cyclohexylamine are dissolved in methanol and made up to 1 liter. The solution is standardized potentiometrically against benzoic acid in aqueous solution (the benzoic acid is first dissolved in a little methanol).]

Glass and calomel electrodes

Measuring instrument or recorder

Procedure: Approximately 8 meq of the acid are dissolved in about 50 ml of methanol, and the potentiometric titration is carried out in the usual manner.

Evaluation: The first potentiometric break corresponds to sulfuric acid (first stage), hydrochloric acid, nitric acid, perchloric acid, organic sulfonic acids, and monoesters of sulfuric acid.

The second potentiometric break corresponds to sulfuric acid (second stage), phosphoric acid (first stage; the others are not titratable), oxalic acid (first stage), phthalic acid (first stage; the second is not titratable), and maleic acid (first stage; the second is not titratable).

The third potentiometric break corresponds to oxalic acid (second stage) and carboxylic acids (not very pronounced).

Variant (268a): Mixtures of nitric acid and carboxylic acids can also be determined with indicators, by titration in methanol solution with 1 N alcoholic potassium hydroxide solution. The indicator for the mineral acid is benzenesulfonic acid-α-azonaphthylamine, while that used afterward for the carboxylic acids is thymol blue (or a similar indicator with a color change in the alkaline range). The titration can be carried out with a single sample, the thymol blue being added after the first color change.

Conversion of the Salts into Free Acids by Ion Exchange (268)

Preparation of the Column: Dowex 50 (or some other strongly acidic ion exchanger), in the form of an aqueous slurry, is introduced into a chromatographic column about 30 cm long and 2 cm in diameter, the slurry being stirred to avoid inclusion of air. The exchanger is converted into the acidic form by washing with 5% hydrochloric acid, and is then washed with water until the eluate is neutral. A final wash with methanol replaces adhering water with methanol.

Approximately 0.5 gm of salt is dissolved in 3 ml of water and introduced into the column. The solution is just allowed to seep into the exchanger, and then a further 3 ml of water are introduced. Finally, the column is eluted with a total of 150 ml of methanol at a moderate speed, and the eluate is titrated with 1 N cyclohexylamine solution.

VIII. Special Alkalimetric Determinations

1. DETERMINATION OF SALTS AND AMINO ACIDS

Salts can be detected by direct alkalimetric titration only if they have a sufficiently high over-all acidity. This condition is satisfied only by salts of weak bases. The acid from which the salt is derived need not be too strong, since weak acids can also be determined if the solvent is chosen correctly. In addition to these properties, the salt must also be sufficiently soluble.

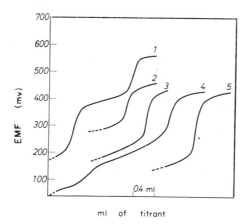

FIG. 63. Potentiometric titration of amino acids in pyridine with 0.1 N tetrabutylammonium hydroxide; glass and calomel electrodes. The samples were dissolved first in a little water. 1, glutamic acid; 2, alanine; 3, arginine hydrochloride; 4, histidine monohydrochloride; 5, glycylglycine. [Cundiff and Markunas (247).]

The applications of the method are fairly sharply bounded by these conditions. They include practically all amine salts, including the amino acids in the betaine form (247). The only salts of this type that cannot be determined by this method are the salts of very strongly basic amines, i.e., mainly quaternary ammonium compounds. Even the guanidine salts of strong acids can be determined. Little work has been done as yet on the determination of salts of heavy metals (e.g., copper), which is possible in principle. Solution difficulties are likely to be encountered in this case, particularly as a result of the formation of basic salts. However, it may be possible to avoid these difficulties by the use of a complexing solvent (ethylenediamine). An example of a determination of this type is the titration of oxine complexes of various metals in ethylenediamine with potassium methoxide (269).

Ethylenediamine and dimethylformamide are used as solvents (254). Ethylenediamine has the advantage that the sample may be dissolved first in a little water, so that practically all amine salts can be dissolved in this way. Only carbonates, oxalates, and phosphates form insoluble precipitates on dilution with ethylenediamine, making the titration impossible. A disadvantage of this solvent is its strong tendency to absorb CO_2.

Dimethylformamide is almost completely free from this disadvantage, and is therefore much more convenient to use. However, water must not be used in the dissolution process, since the results of the titration will otherwise be too high, owing to hydrolysis. Salts of polybasic acids and some salts of lower aliphatic amines (and ammonia) with monobasic acids (e.g., ammonium chloride, ammonium acetate, butylamine hydrochloride) are insoluble in dimethylformamide in the dry state, and so cannot be determined in this solvent.

The titrant is a solution of sodium methoxide in methanol/benzene. The end point can be detected with indicators. Azo violet is used in all titrations in ethylenediamine. For titrations in dimethylformamide, either thymol blue (salts of mineral acids) or azo violet (salts of carboxylic acids) is used, depending on the acidity of the salt.

Cundiff and Markunas (270) have described an elegant method for the determination of salts of strong bases (e.g., alkali metal salts) with weak acids, which cannot be titrated directly owing to their low acidities. The salt is dissolved in excess aqueous sulfuric acid, and the solution is diluted with pyridine. The sparingly soluble sulfates precipitate out, and the acids in the clear solution that remains are determined by titration with tetrabutylammonium hydroxide. The excess sulfuric acid is also determined as a dibasic acid, but the quantity present can be calculated from the quantity of alkali required to reach the first potentiometric break (first stage of sulfuric acid) (cf. also Chapter 5, Section VII,2).

Determination of Salts of Weak Bases (254)

Reagents:

System I:
  Ethylenediamine
  Azo violet, saturated solution in benzene

System II:
  Dimethylformamide
  Thymol blue, 0.3% in methanol
  Azo violet, saturated solution in benzene

  0.1 N sodium methoxide (or potassium methoxide) solution

Procedure: System I (for sparingly soluble salts): 0.4 to 0.9 meq of the substance is dissolved in about 1 ml of water; the solution is then diluted with about 20 ml of preneutralized ethylenediamine and titrated in the presence of azo violet until the color changes to pure blue, care being taken to exclude atmospheric carbon dioxide from the solution. If more water is required, the quantity of ethylenediamine must also be increased, since the ratio of water to ethylenediamine must not exceed 1:15. Aqueous solutions can also be analyzed in this way if the concentration of the salts is sufficiently high. If the salts are sufficiently soluble in ethylenediamine, no water need be used.

System II (for more soluble salts): 20 ml of dimethylformamide containing a little indicator are titrated to the color change. The sample (0.4 to 0.9 meq) is dissolved in this solution and titrated in the usual manner. Thymol blue is used as the indicator for the salts of strong acids, and azo violet for the salts of weak acids. If the titration is carried out quickly, it is not absolutely essential to exclude air.

Variants: The titration can also be carried out potentiometrically with tetrabutylammonium hydroxide as the titrant. For the determination of amino acids and their hydrochlorides (two stages!), the sample was dissolved in water and diluted with pyridine (247).

Determination of Salts of Strong Bases (270)

Reagents and Apparatus:
  Pyridine
  Acetone
  1 N aqueous sulfuric acid
  0.1 N tetrabutylammonium hydroxide solution

Glass and calomel electrodes

Measuring instrument or recorder

Procedure: The substance (0.5 meq) is weighed into a 100-ml graduated flask and dissolved in 1 ml of water + 2 ml of sulfuric acid (up to 3 ml more of water may be added if required). The solution is made up to the mark with pyridine or acetone (preferably the former). As soon as the precipitated sulfates have settled, 50 ml of the clear solution are withdrawn with a pipet and titrated potentiometrically in the usual manner, in the absence of air. The first potentiometric break corresponds to the excess sulfuric acid (as a monobasic acid), and the second break to the second stage of the sulfuric acid together with the acid to be determined. The blank titer of the solvent must be taken into account.

2. DETERMINATION OF ENOLS AND IMIDES

These compounds have acidities between those of carboxylic acids and those of phenols, and can therefore be determined alkalimetrically with color indicators. The systems used are dimethylformamide/thymol blue (I), dimethylformamide/azo violet (II), and ethylenediamine/*o*-nitroaniline (III), depending on the acidity of the sample; system III is used for very weak acids with acidities of the same order as that of phenol.* The titrant is 0.1 N potassium methoxide solution. The chemical and structural conditions governing titratability have been described by Fritz (244).

Enols

Groupings of the form A—CH$_2$—A' are titratable if each of A and A' is one of the following:

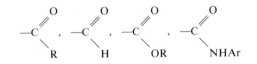

A and A' may also be —C ≡ N. The carboxamide group is less effective, and titration is possible only if the other activating group is more strongly electron-attracting (e.g., as in cyanoacetamide). The carboxyl group is practically without effect, so that cyanoacetic acid, for example,

*For procedures, see Chapter 5, Section VI, 1, 2.

can only be titrated as a monobasic acid. On the other hand, the azomethine group —C=N— appears to be effective in many cases.

Compounds containing the grouping A—CH₂—CH₂—A' are not acidic, and α-diketones (—CO—CO—CH₂—) are also untitratable. A survey of the compounds analyzed leads to Table 7, the Roman numerals indicating the system used (see above).

TABLE 7

Compound	System
Acetoacetanilide	II
Cyanoacetamide	III
Dibenzoylmethane	I
Ethyl cyanoacetate	II
Diethyl malonate[a]	II
Malonodinitrile	II
Dimedone	II
1-Phenyl-3-carboethoxy-5-pyrazolone	II

[a] Concerning substituted malonates, see Chapter 5, Section VIII,3.

Imides

Groupings with the structure A—NH—A' (where A and A' may be

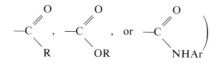

can be titrated. If one of the two groups is

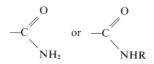

the titratability is uncertain; examples of this type are acetylurea and hydantoin, only the latter being titratable (Table 8).

The acidity is appreciably increased by the replacement of the oxygen in the carbonyl function with sulfur, or by the introduction of a second carbonyl group (oxanilide is titratable, whereas diphenylurea is not).

TABLE 8

Compound	System
s-Diphenylthiourea	II
Dithiobiuret	II
Dithiooxamide	II
Hydantoin	II
Phthalimide	II
Succinimide	II
1-Phenyl-3-cyclohexylthiourea	III
1-Phenyl-3-naphthylthiourea	II
1-Phenyl-3-(2-pyrimidyl)thiourea	II
Theobromine (in the presence of caffeine[a])	Pyridine/azo violet or ethylenediamine/azo violet
Thiobarbituric acid	I

[a]Caffeine possesses no acidic properties.

In addition to these visual methods, it is naturally also possible to use potentiometric methods, and these are greatly preferred in the titration of unknown mixtures. The most important solvents are pyridine and dimethylformamide, and the titrant is tetrabutylammonium hydroxide. Thus the compounds listed in Table 9 have been titrated in pyridine by this method (262) (Fig. 64).

TABLE 9

Compound	Notes
Cyanamide Dicyandiamide	In the same solution
Biuret	The titer was only 50% of the theoretical value
Benzotriazole	—
Phthalimide	—
Succinimide	—
Barbituric acid	—
Cyanuric acid	—

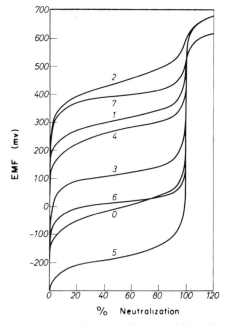

FIG. 64. Potentiometric titration of weak acids in pyridine with 0.1 N tetrabutylammonium hydroxide; glass and calomel electrodes: 0, benzoic acid; 1, cyanamide; 2, dicyandiamide; 3, phthalimide; 4, succinimide; 5, barbituric acid; 6, cyanuric acid; 7, nitromethane. [Streuli (262).]

For procedures, see Chapter 5, Section VI,2.

Cluett (271) has titrated substituted phenylureas in butylamine.

3. DETERMINATION OF MALONIC ESTERS (UNSUBSTITUTED AND MONOSUBSTITUTED IN THE PRESENCE OF ONE ANOTHER) (272)

Malonic esters can be titrated as weak acids because of their active methylene group (see Chapter 5, Section VIII,2). Since the acidity constants of the unsubstituted esters differ from those of the monosubstituted esters by a factor of from 50 to 100 (273), it is even possible to carry out selective determinations. Disubstituted esters are neutral, and so cannot be titrated.

Difficulties may arise because small quantities of malonic esters in alkylmalonic esters cannot be determined, since these have a blank titer of from 2 to 13%, depending on the substance.* An improvement

---

*For further details, see original publication.

would probably result from the use of potentiometric end-point detection instead of the indicator method described.

The accuracy obtainable is about ±1 to 2%.

Determination of Diethyl Malonate in the Presence of Monosubstituted and Disubstituted Esters

Reagents:
Dimethylformamide
0.1 N potassium methoxide solution
Azo violet, saturated solution in benzene

Procedure: Dimethylformamide (15 to 20 ml) containing from 4 to 6 drops of indicator solution is titrated to the color change. The sample (0.5 to 1 meq), calculated on the basis of titratable ester, is added to this solution, and the titration is continued until the same tint is reached again. Small contents cannot be determined, owing to the blank titer of the monosubstituted esters.

Determination of Total Diethyl Malonate and Monosubstituted Esters

Reagents:
Ethylenediamine
0.1 N potassium methoxide solution
o-Nitroaniline, 0.5% in benzene

The procedure is similar to that used for the determination of phenols (see Chapter 5, Section VI,2).

4. DETERMINATION OF SULFONAMIDES

Owing to the weakly acidic properties of the SO_2NH grouping, sulfonamides can be determined by direct alkalimetric titration. It is even possible, to some extent, to separate mixtures on the basis of the influence of the group adjacent to the nitrogen on the acidity. Aromatic groups, and particularly the thiazole ring in sulfathiazole, greatly increase acidity, whereas aliphatic groups and hydrogen in particular (in sulfanilamide) keep the acidity down to the same order of magnitude as that of phenols.

On the basis of these properties, it is even possible to carry out titrations with indicators (274). More strongly acidic sulfonamides with aromatic or heteroaromatic substituents directly attached to the nitrogen are titrated in dimethylformamide with sodium methoxide, and with thymol blue as the indicator (see Chapter 5, Section VI,1). The more weakly acidic derivatives, on the other hand, are titrated in butylamine, with azo violet as the indicator (see Chapter 5, Section VI,2). The same method can in principle be used for the selective determination of mixtures, but this is better carried out by a potentiometric method (187), in which the solvent is acetone and the titrant is triethylbutylammonium hydroxide (Fig. 65).

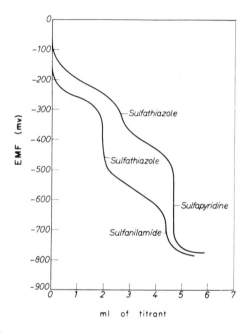

FIG. 65. Potentiometric titration of sulfonamides in acetone with 0.1 N triethylbutylammonium hydroxide; glass and calomel electrodes. [Fritz and Yamamura (187).]

The common sulfonamides listed in Table 10 have been determined by the visual method.

Many unusual derivatives have also been titrated with very good reproducibility. The only compound of this group that is not acidic is sulfaguanidine, which cannot therefore be titrated.

In addition to this aklalimetric method, an acidimetric method is also known; this method is not based on the sulfonamide grouping, but on any amino groups that may be present. It involves potentiometric titration in glacial acetic acid (275).

TABLE 10

Compound	Method
Sulfamethazine	Dimethylformamide/azo violet
Sulfamerazine	Dimethylformamide/azo violet
Sulfadiazine	Dimethylformamide/azo violet
Sulfapyridine	Dimethylformamide/thymol blue
Sulfathalidine	Dimethylformamide/azo violet
Sulfathiazole	Dimethylformamide/azo violet
Sulfanilimide	Butylamine/azo violet

5. Determination of 2,4-Dinitrophenylhydrazones (276)

A common method for the determination of carbonyl compounds is by precipitation of the sparingly soluble dinitrophenylhydrazones. The precipitate may then be weighed, or the excess reagent may be determined by a reductometric back-titration (277, 278).

The uses of the two methods are not identical, since the equivalent weight of the carbonyl compound enters into the calculation in the first method, but not in the second. Thus if the equivalent weight is unknown, it is necessary either to use the second method or to determine the equivalent weight of the precipitate obtained in the first method.

This is generally found by elementary analysis, but an alkalimetric method is also available. Dinitrophenylhydrazones, like dinitrophenyl-hydrazine itself, are weak acids,* and can be titrated potentiometrically in pyridine with tetrabutylammonium hydroxide. Since the quantity of substance available is generally small, the method was developed for use on the micro scale. If the molecular weight is known, on the other hand, the titration method can be used instead of weighing.

The only source of possible error appears to be that associated with the actual precipitation of the dinitrophenylhydrazone. Interference results if the hydrazones are too soluble or if the condensation is incomplete because of steric hindrance. However, the titration itself is simple and elegant. It cannot be carried out with indicators, since the solution assumes an intense red color owing to salt formation with the hydrazone. It is essential that air should be excluded.

If several functional groups are present, several potentiometric breaks

*No data are available regarding their strength, but it appears to lie between those of carboxylic acids and of phenols.

are obtained. This is the case, e.g., with bisdinitrophenylhydrazones (glyoxal) and with derivatives of ketocarboxylic acids (α-ketoglutaric acid) and aldehydrophenols (vanillin). The quantity of base required is accordingly higher, and must be taken into account in the calculation. These compounds can also be determined selectively in certain circumstances (Table 11).

TABLE 11

CARBONYL COMPOUNDS STUDIED AS DINITROPHENYLHYDRAZONES

Formaldehyde	1-Hydroxy-2-butanone acetate
Crotonaldehyde	Acetoacetic ester
Isovaleraldehyde	
Furfural	*Bifunctional compounds:*
p-Isopropylbenzaldehyde	Glyoxal
Benzaldehyde	2,5-Hexanedione
Acetone	Butanedione
n-Propyl methyl ketone	2,3-Pentanedione
Acetophenone	Vanillin
3-Pentanone	α-Ketoglutaric acid
Cyclohexanone	

p-Nitrophenylhydrazones, phenylhydrazones, phenylosazones, and aldehyde-dimedone condensation products can also be titrated in the same way as dinitrophenylhydrazones.

The method permits the titration of 1 to 2 mg of substance with an accuracy of ±2%.

Reagents and Apparatus:

Pyridine*

0.01 or 0.02 N tetrabutylammonium hydroxide (100 or 200 ml of 0.1 N solution are mixed with 30 ml of methanol and made up to 1 liter with benzene. The solution is standardized against benzoic acid.)

Glass and calomel electrodes

Measuring instrument or recorder

Procedure: The hydrazone (2 to 20 mg) is dissolved in 50 ml of pyridine and titrated potentiometrically in the usual manner in the ab-

*Acetone, acetonitrile, and dimethylformamide can also be used, but these are less suitable.

sence of air. The blank titer of the solvent is found in the same way and subtracted from the result.

6. DETERMINATION OF ALKOXYL GROUPS

Analyses of this nature are generally carried out by reaction with strong hydriodic acid, as described by Zeisel. The alkyl iodides formed can be determined by various methods (279). A method that was recently introduced involves alkalimetric titration in pyridine. An advantage of this method is that any hydrogen iodide distilled over with the alkyl iodide does not interfere, so that the washing required in other methods is no longer necessary.

Principle of the Method: The alkyl iodides formed in the reaction with hydrogen iodide are driven in a stream of nitrogen into a flask containing pyridine (the gas stream may or may not first be passed through a wash liquid). When absorption is complete, the pyridine solution is boiled for 2 minutes to quaternize the iodides:

$$RI + C_5H_5N \rightarrow [C_5H_5N-R] \, I$$

The resulting salt can be titrated as a weak acid in pyridine. Hydriodic acid can be selectively determined as a strong acid (Fig. 66). The titration is not affected by any hydrogen sulfide that may distil over.

Some times required for complete reaction of a 10- to 15-mg sample are:

methoxyl	45 minutes
ethoxyl	60 minutes
butoxyl	120 minutes

The titration is carried out with 0.02 N tetrabutylammonium hydroxide solution, either potentiometrically or with azo violet as the indicator. This indicator has two color changes: first from yellow to red, and then from red to blue. In both methods, the difference between the first and second end points is used for the calculation. For the detailed procedures, see the original literature (280).

7. DETERMINATION OF 3,5-DINITROBENZOATES

In the characterization of alcohols, the esters of 3,5-dinitrobenzoic acid play a part similar to that of the dinitrophenylhydrazones in the characterization of carbonyl compounds. It may again be necessary in this case to analyze the derivative in order to find the molecular weight of the original alcohol. As in the determination of dinitrophenylhydrazones, this can be achieved by alkalimetric titration.

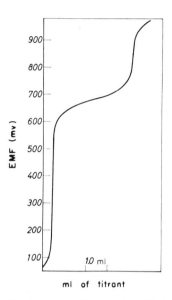

ml of titrant

FIG. 66. Potentiometric titration of a mixture of hydriodic acid and butyl iodide in pyridine with 0.02 N tetrabutylammonium hydroxide solution; glass and calomel electrodes. [Cundiff and Markunas (280).]

Dinitrobenzoates behave in pyridine as weak acids.* Since the neutralization product has an intense red color, the end point is preferably found potentiometrically. Quantitative results can be obtained only if the solution is boiled some time, particularly in the analysis of higher alcohols.

A hydroxyl group determination is carried out by direct reaction of alcohols with a solution of dinitrobenzoyl chloride in pyridine, followed by titration:

$$ROH + C_6H_3(NO_2)_2COCl \rightarrow R \cdot OOCC_6H_3(NO_2)_2 + HCl$$
$$H_2O + C_6H_3(NO_2)_2COCl \rightarrow C_6H_3(NO_2)_2COOH + HCl$$

This determination makes use of the fact that the hydrochloric acid–dinitrobenzoic acid mixture formed by the hydrolysis of excess acyl chloride behaves as a strong acid, and can therefore be distinguished from the ester (Fig. 67). Thus the potentiometric titration gives two potentiometric breaks, and the difference between the titers at these breaks corresponds to the quantity of ester present. The titration may also be stopped at the first potentiometric break, but the concentration of the

*For the structure of the salts formed on neutralization, see Chapter 5, Section VIII,9.

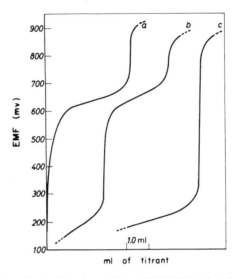

FIG. 67. Potentiometric titrations in pyridine with 0.2 *N* tetrabutylammonium hydroxide solution; glass and calomel electrodes: *a,* ethyl 3,5-dinitrobenzoate; *b,* ethyl 3,5-dinitrobenzoate + 3,5-dinitrobenzoyl chloride; *c,* 3,5-dinitrobenzoyl chloride. [Robinson *et al.* (282).]

original dinitrobenzoyl chloride solution must then be determined accurately, and the difference corresponds to the alchol content. This determination can also be carried out visually without indicators, since the point at which the neutralization of the ester begins (first potentiometric break) is marked by a red coloration of the solution. Thus the esters act as indicators for the determination of the strong acids present. Tertiary alcohols are also included in the titration if the reaction time is increased to 24–48 hours.

Titration of 3,5-Dinitrobenzoates (281)

Reagents and Apparatus:
   0.01 *N* tetrabutylammonium hydroxide solution (prepared as described
      in Chapter 5, Section VIII,5)
   Pyridine
   Glass and calomel electrodes
   Measuring instrument or recorder

Procedure: The ester (2 to 20 mg) is dissolved in 50 ml of pyridine in a 125-ml Erlenmeyer flask with a reflux condenser (ground-glass joints), and refluxed for 30 minutes. When cool, the solution is washed into a beaker with the aid of a little pyridine, and titrated potentiometrically under nitrogen in the usual manner. The blank titer is found in the same way and subtracted from the result.

Determination of the OH Value of an Alcohol
by Reaction with 3,5-Dinitrobenzoyl Chloride (282)

Reagents and Apparatus:
    Pyridine
    3,5-Dinitrobenzoyl chloride, 98 to 100% (the reagent is stored in the form of a fine powder in a desiccator)
    0.2 N tetrabutylammonium hydroxide solution in benzene/methanol (7:1). [Preparation: as described for a 0.1 N solution, except that the quantity of reagent is doubled and 300 ml of methanol are used. The solution is purified by passage through an anion exchanger (see Chapter 5, Section III,2) at a rate of from 7 to 10 ml/minute.]
    Measuring instrument or recorder

Procedure: A 0.2 N solution of dinitrobenzoyl chloride in pyridine is freshly prepared for each set of analyses. The solution consists of 1.15 gm of the reagent dissolved in 25 ml of pyridine, with gentle heating (the titer need not be determined accurately).

In the case of liquid samples, approximately 4 meq are pipetted into a 10-ml graduated flask containing 3 ml of pyridine. Care should be taken to avoid wetting the neck of the flask. The flask, which has previously been tared, is reweighed to find the exact weight of its contents. It is then made up to the mark with pyridine.

For the actual determination, approximately 0.4 meq of a solid sample, or 1.0 ml of the above solution in the case of a liquid sample, is placed in a 125-ml Erlenmeyer flask with ground-glass joints; 4.0 ml of the acyl chloride reagent are added, and the flask is then tightly stoppered, shaken gently to dissolve the sample, and allowed to stand for 15 minutes; 7 to 10 drops of water are then added. A blank titration is carried out with 4 ml of reagent and 7 to 10 drops of water.

Visual Titration: Pyridine (40 ml) is added to the reaction mixture; the solution is then brought almost to the boiling point, cooled, and titrated. The end point is indicated by a persistent red coloration of the solution. The blank titration is carried out in the same way, and the number of OH groups present is found from the difference.

Potentiometric Titration: 25 ml of pyridine are added to the reaction mixture and the solution is brought almost to the boiling point. When cool, the solution is transferred to a 250-ml beaker, and the original flask is carefully washed with two 10-ml portions of pyridine. The potentiometric titration is then carried out under nitrogen. After the first potentiometric break, the titrant must be added slowly. The result is calculated either from the difference between the blank and the first potentiometric break (as in the visual titration) or from the difference between the two potentiometric breaks. In the latter case, no blank titration is required.

8. DETERMINATION OF PHENOL ESTERS

When these esters are dissolved in ethylenediamine, they appear to undergo aminolysis:

$$R—COOAr + H_2N—CH_2—CH_2—NH_2 \longrightarrow ArOH + H_2N—CH_2—CH_2—NHCOOR$$

The free phenols formed in this way can be titrated as acids (283).

Phenol esters of aliphatic [but not of aromatic (284)] acids can be titrated in acetone with tetrabutylammonium hydroxide.

9. DETERMINATION OF NITRO COMPOUNDS

a. Alphatic Nitro Compounds

Little work has so far been carried out on compounds of this class, since they are of little practical importance. However, alkalimetric titration of these compounds should be possible owing to the formation of aci forms:

This has been shown to be true in the case of nitromethane, with which satisfactory potentiometric breaks were obtained in pyridine (262) and in butylamine (252).

b. Nitroaromatic Amines

The fact that *o*-nitroaniline can be used as an indicator in the titration of very weak acids shows that this compound possesses a certain acidity. This is due to the extremely strong electron-repelling nature of the nitro group. Whereas the intensification of the acidity of phenols by nitro groups was known and studied a long time ago, little attention has been paid so far to the corresponding phenomenon in aniline derivatives.

Fritz *et al.* (285) studied a number of aniline and diphenylamine derivatives (see Table 12), using pyridine as the solvent and triethyl-

TABLE 12

Compound	Remarks
m-Nitroaniline	No reaction
o-Nitroaniline	Reacts, but not titratable
p-Nitroaniline	Reacts, but not titratable
2-Chloro-4-nitroaniline	Slight inflection of the curve
4-Chloro-2-nitroaniline	Titratable
2,6-Dichloro-4-nitroaniline	Readily titratable
2,4-Dinitroaniline	Readily titratable
Picramide	Very readily titratable
2-Nitrodiphenylamine	Slight inflection of the curve
4-Nitrodiphenylamine	Titratable
2,4-Dinotrodiphenylamine	Readily titratable
2,2′,4,4′,6,6′-Hexanitrodiphenylamine	Dibasic, first break very sharp

butylammonium hydroxide as the titrant. The end point was detected potentiometrically (Fig. 68).

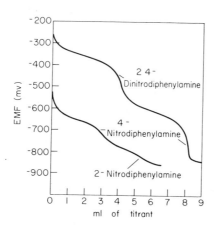

Fig. 68. Potentiometric titrations of nitrodiphenylamines in pyridine with triethylbutyl-ammonium hydroxide; glass and calomel electrodes. [Fritz *et al.* (285).]

The difference in the acidities is so large that a number of simultaneous determinations are possible. The second potentiometric break of hexanitrodiphenylamine is of interest, since it cannot be traced to a dissociable proton. It must be assumed that the factors involved are those responsible for the acidity of polyaromatic compounds in general.

c. *Aromatic Polynitro Compounds*

It has long been known that aromatic polynitro compounds (e.g., 1,3,5-trinitrobenzene) possess acidic properties; e.g., they dissolve in alkali solutions to give a red coloration. However, this is due not to the dissociation of a proton, but to adduct formation between the base and the polynitro compound. Meisenheimer (286) demonstrated the structure of the 1:1 adduct in the case of 2,4,6-trinitrophenetole. Further addition should proceed in the same manner to give the 1:2 and 1:3 adducts (trinitrophenetole is tribasic):

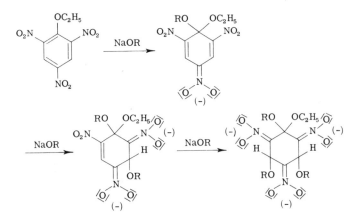

The simplest member of this class is *m*-dinitrobenzene, nitrobenzene itself having no appreciable acidic properties. Titrations of polynitro compounds have been carried out potentiometrically with the sodium salt of ethanolamine in ethylenediamine (287, 288) and with triethylbutylammonium hydroxide in pyridine (285) (Fig. 69; see Table 13).

The titrations in ethylenediamine were carried out with antimony indicator electrodes (see Chapter 5, Section IX,1,a,α) (287), whereas the determinations in pyridine were carried out by the procedure used for the titration of acids in pyridine with tetrabutylammonium hydroxide (see Chapter 5, Section VI,2).

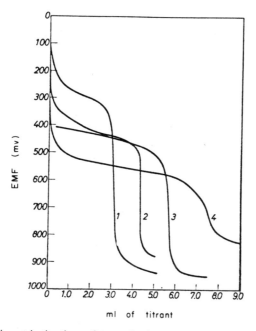

FIG. 69. Potentiometric titrations of aromatic nitro compounds in pyridine with triethylbutylammonium hydroxide; glass and calomel electrodes: 1, 2,4,6-trinitrotoluene; 2, 1,3,5-trinitrobenzene; 3, 2-bromo-4,6-dinitrotoluene; 4, 2,4-dinitrotulene. [Fritz *et al.* (285).]

A point of special interest for the elucidation of constitution is the fact that the 2,4-dinitrophenyl derivatives of alcohols, phenols, mercaptans, and amines can be titrated with tetrabutylammonium hydroxide in acetone or pyridine (289). These derivatives can be readily prepared in most

TABLE 13

Compound	Remarks	Ref.
m-Dinitrobenzene	Dibasic, two potentiometric breaks	(287)
1,3,5-Trinitrobenzene	Monobasic	(285)
Picric acid	Tribasic, one potentiometric break	(287)
2,4,6-Trinitro-*m*-cresol	Tribasic, two potentiometric breaks	(287)
2,4,6-Trinitrophenetole	Tribasic, two potentiometric breaks	(287)
2,4-Dinitrotoluene	Monobasic (not very reproducible)	(285)
2,4,6-Trinitrotoluene	Monobasic	(285)
2-Bromo-4,6-dinitrotoluene	Monobasic	(285)

cases by reaction with dinitrofluorobenzene, and can be used for characterization of the compounds mentioned. The mean equivalent weight can then be readily found from the titration.

d. *Explosives*

Explosives can contain:

nitrates	ammonium nitrate
	sodium nitrate
esters of nitric acid	nitroglycerin
	nitrocellulose
	pentaerythritol tetranitrate
nitro compounds	trinitrotoluene
	dinitrotoluene
	nitrotoluene
	Hexogen (hexahydro-1,3,5-trinitro-*s*-triazine)

All these compounds can, in principle, be titrated. In the case of mixtures, the salts are first separated from the organic compounds by extraction with methyl isobutyl ketone (290). The total nitrate is found by titration with perchloric acid in glacial acetic acid/chloroform, and ammonium nitrate is determined by alkalimetric titration in dimethylformamide.

Selective determination of the organic compounds is possible only in certain cases. The reader is referred to the original literature for details of the complicated procedures. The determinations are always carried out by potentiometric titration with tetrabutylammonium hydroxide in various solvents. In some cases, several potentiometric breaks are observed.

10. DETERMINATION OF HYDROGEN PEROXIDE AND HYDROPEROXIDES

The —O—OH grouping is considerably more acidic than the ordinary hydroxyl group. Consequently, hydroperoxides (including hydrogen peroxide) are almost as strongly acidic as phenols [$pK_A = 11.6$ to 12.8 (291, 292)]. In most cases, therefore, they can still be titrated with strong bases.

On the other hand, peracids are less acidic than the corresponding carboxylic acids (difference ~ 3.5 pK units). For example, peracetic acid has a pK_A value of 8.2; i.e., it is only slightly more acidic than phenol.

The alkalimetric titration of these compounds is of particular interest, since it may provide a means of distinguishing between the various peroxide configurations, a distinction that is difficult to make by other methods.

The titration is carried out in ethylenediamine with the sodium salt of ethanolamine as the titrant (293). Two antimony indicator electrodes are used in the potentiometric titration, one being placed in the stream of titrant from the buret, and so acting as a reference electrode (tip of buret immersed).

Note that the acidity of hydrogen peroxide is increased in ethylenediamine, so that selective determinations can be carried out in the presence of hydroperoxides (this had at first seemed impossible purely on the grounds of the pK_A values).

The accuracy obtained with from 1 to 10 meq of peroxide samples was about ±2%. However, it is likely that the method will be very sensitive to impurities with a reducing action, since peroxides in alkaline solution are very strong oxidizing agents.

11. DETERMINATION OF MERCAPTANS

Since the SH group is appreciably more acidic than the OH group, mercaptans and, above all, thiophenols can be determined without much difficulty by alkalimetric titration. Fritz and Lisicki (252) determined thiophenol in butylamine with sodium methoxide as the titrant and thymol blue as the indicator. o-Mercaptotoluene can also be determined potentiometrically in pyridine with tetrabutylammonium hydroxide (247). The present author has shown that dodecyl mercaptan can be titrated in acetone with tetrabutylammonium hydroxide.

However, none of these methods is of much interest, since much more specific and more sensitive methods such as argentometry and idometry are available (see Chapter 5, Section IX,11). Thus alkalimetry is seriously considered only in special cases for the determination of mercaptans.

12. DETERMINATION OF ACETYLENES

The tendency of the grouping $-C \equiv CH$ to form sparingly soluble heavy metal salts has already been used in a number of cases for analytical determinations. The reagents used are copper, mercury, and in particular silver salts. Precautions are taken to avoid isolation of the salts, which are explosive. If a concentrated silver nitrate solution is used, the acetylides remain in solution in the form of complexes (294). They are determined by alkalimetric titration of the nitric acid liberated, methyl purple being used as the indicator. The accurate recognition of the end point is rather critical owing to the high concentration of silver ions (2.5 *N*), but can be improved by the use of potentiometric methods. Owing to the danger that the sintered-glass diaphragm may become blocked by precipitated silver chloride, the calomel reference electrode should be replaced by a mercurous sulfate electrode. Methanol may be used as the solvent instead of water if the sample is dissolved in a solvent that is immiscible with water. In this case the acetylides formed still generally remain in solution. The titrant is a 1 *N* solution of silver perchlorate in methanol (295). After the reaction, the acid formed is titrated with a standard solution of trihydroxymethylaminomethane in methanol, with a mixture of thymol blue and alphazurine as the indicator. This method can also be used on the micro scale, in which case Martius yellow is used as the indicator (296). The reproducibility is ±0.5%, and the accuracy is ±1%.

13. Determination of Carbon Dioxide in Gases

The classic determination of carbon dioxide by absorption in excess barium hydroxide solution and back-titration with acid can be replaced by determination in nonaqueous media. Advantages of this method are:

(1) The use of a basic solvent (which also acts as the absorbent) permits direct alkalimetric titration.
(2) Owing to the much better solubility of carbon dioxide in many organic solvents than in water, higher gas flow rates can be used in the absorption process.
(3) This method also gives very accurate results in microdeterminations.

In spite of the relatively favorable conditions for the absorption of carbon dioxide, it is usually necessary to use a special absorption vessel. This vessel may be an impinger wash bottle (297), or preferably a special spiral wash bottle (298) with a small volume (Fig. 70).

The principle of the absorption process is the reaction of carbon dioxide with an amine to form an amine carbamate:

$$2 \ R\!-\!NH_2 + CO_2 \longrightarrow RNH - COOH \cdot H_2N\!-\!R$$

In a solvent with a sufficiently low basicity, this salt behaves as a monobasic acid, and can therefore be titrated with sodium (or potassium) methoxide solution.

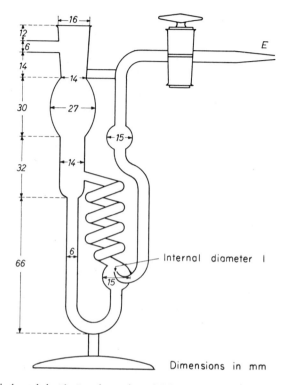

FIG. 70. Spiral wash bottle for absorption of CO_2; *E:* gas inlet. [Blom and Edelhausen (298).]

Deckert (297) used a 25% solution of ammonia in alcohol at −80°C as the solvent. The indicator used was thymolphthalein. A mixture of alcohol, dioxane, and benzylamine can be used at room temperature (299).

A solution of ethanolamine in pyridine can also be used, but alkali must be added to the absorption solution from time to time during the absorption, in order to avoid losses. With 0.02 N sodium methoxide solution as the titrant and thymol blue as the indicator, it is possible to achieve an accuracy of 0.001 ml, corresponding to 0.2 μg of carbon (300). The titration volume in this case is 2 ml. Pure amines may also be used. Thus the determination can be carried out in ethylenediamine (300a) with a 0.1 N solution of potassium methoxide in methanol/benzene (indicator: Celliton Fast Orange) and in benzylamine (301) (indicator: thymol blue).

IX. Special Fields

1. MICRO- AND ULTRAMICRODETERMINATIONS

The number of procedures described in the literature is not very great. This is probably due largely to the small demand, since these methods have been mainly used for industrial or pharmaceutical products, which are available in sufficiently large quantities to permit the use of normal methods. Another factor opposing the wider application is the fact that these methods are much more sensitive than semimicro or macro methods to the blank titer nearly always possessed by the solvent and to the sharpness of the end point, which is usually poorer than in water. The blank titer of the solvent has a particularly disturbing effect on the determination of weak acids, owing to the presence of atmospheric carbon dioxide. The quantity of solvent used is kept to a minimum in order to oppose this effect (302), and this measure also leads to improved end-point recognition. This last aspect is particularly important in ultramicrodeterminations, in which special apparatus is used to permit a marked reduction of the titration volume, while the conditions regarding the concentrations used remain similar as in macrodeterminations. The quantities of solvent used are of the order of 1 ml (the quantities of substance are from 50 to 1000 μg), and the titrant solution is introduced from special piston burets, which can measure the solution with an accuracy of a fraction of a microliter. It is therefore possible to use relatively concentrated solutions (0.01 to 0.1 N). Thus the sharpness of the end point obtainable in potentiometric titrations is comparable to that obtained in an ordinary determination. However, this is not the case with color indicators, since the thickness of the layer through which the light passes is smaller, and the quantity of indicator used must therefore be larger. This generally reduces the sharpness of the color change (see Chapter 2, Section VI). Nevertheless, the accuracies obtained by the two methods are approximately equal. This is probably due to the time factor, since the titration with indicators can be carried out more rapidly. This is particularly important in ultramicrodeterminations, in which surface phenomena (particularly evaporation and adhesion) are very important because of the small volumes used. Thus in one case the loss of 0.01 N perchloric acid in glacial acetic acid by evaporation from an ultramicroburet in the course of 90 minutes was 4.4 μl, i.e., about 10% of the quantity added during the determination (303). This effect is much less pronounced in aqueous solutions, evidently because the surface tension and wetting properties differ from those of organic liquids.

Microdeterminations are carried out in apparatus similar to that used in macrodeterminations, except that smaller burets (5 to 10 ml) and titration vessels are used. This means that, for the usual 5-mg sample, it is necessary to use relatively dilute titrant solutions (0.005 to 0.05 N). With the usual quantities of solvent (10 to 40 ml), therefore, the concentration conditions are generally less favorable with regard to end-point detection than in ultramicrodeterminations. Thus the only indicator methods that can be used on the micro scale are those with particularly sharp end points. On the other hand, little difficulty is encountered in potentiometric methods, particularly when a recording instrument is used.

There are three principal methods available for the end-point detection, i.e., the classic potentiometric and indicator methods and the recently developed direct spectrophotometric titration without added indicators. This last method is naturally restricted to special cases, since it requires that the substance under examination should possess indicator properties and that it should absorb light sufficiently strongly (see Chapter 2, Section VII). However, it permits the use of very dilute titrant solutions.

a. Special Notes on Microtitrations

α. *Potentiometric End-Point Detection.* The determination is most easily carried out with the aid of a combined glass/calomel electrode (single-rod measuring cell), which is also available in a form suitable for microanalyses.* A second possibility in the determination of acids is the use of two antimony indicator electrodes; one of these dips into the solution, while the other is in contact with the titrant solution, which is in turn connected to the reaction solution via the immersed buret tip (302). This second electrode therefore acts as a reference electrode. The advantage of this arrangement in microdeterminations is its compactness.

Owing to the relatively small changes in potential, special care must be taken in the determination of the inflection of the potential curve. It is very advantageous to use a recording instrument, provided that it is capable of measuring small volumes of titrant solution with sufficient accuracy. Titration to a given potential, which is regarded as the neutrality point, is not recommended in microdeterminations, since the error due to the nonreproducibility of absolute potentials would be too great.

β. *End-Point Detection with Indicators.* The principles laid down in Chapter 2, Section VI, are even more important in microdeterminations. In particular, the quantity of indicator used must be as small as possible.

*Schott, Mainz.

The titration may be carried out in a tall glass beaker (with a magnetic stirrer) instead of in an Erlenmeyer flask, in order to obtain a sufficiently thick layer of liquid.

Indicators that do not give sharp end points should not be used. This applies in particular to the determination of phenols with o-nitroaniline.

It is recommended that color-comparison solutions should be used to increase the accuracy of the end-point detection. (For the preparation of these solutions, see Chapter 4, Section II,2,a,α.)

γ. *Correction for the Blank Titer of the Solvent.*   This should also include any indicator correction required. A blank titer is nearly always involved, even in the potentiometric titration of bases in glacial acetic acid. Its importance is still greater when basic solvents are used, owing to absorption of carbon dioxide from the atmosphere. In some circumstances, it can even make a determination impossible. In microdeterminations, therefore, special care should be taken with regard to the purity of the solvent.

The correction for the blank titer can be made in one of two ways. In manual potentiometric titrations the blank titer is best found by a special titration, which should preferably be repeated; the same quantity of solvent is then used in all titrations, and the correction is made by subtraction of the blank value. Where indicators are used it is easier and more accurate to titrate the solvent, then add the substance to be analyzed and continue the titration to the same tint.

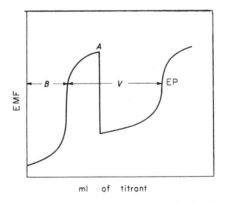

Fig. 71. Elimination of the solvent blank in photometric titration with a recording instrument: A = addition of substance; V = volume of titrant; EP = end point; B = solvent blank.

This principle can also be used when a recording instrument is available. The solvent is first titrated, then the substance is added, and the titration is continued to the end point. The distance between this point and a point having the same potential, and hence the same pH, corresponds to the quantity of titrant solution used (Fig. 71).

δ. *Titration Vessels and Burets.* The determination of bases with perchloric acid is insensitive to atmospheric carbon dioxide, and can therefore be carried out in small beakers with magnetic stirring. The determination of acids, on the other hand, must be carried out in a closed system under a protective gas. In the simplest case, this can be achieved by the use of an Erlenmeyer flask with a lateral gas inlet tube. This apparatus can be used for titrations with indicators. In potentiometric titrations, it is necessary to use a covered vessel with several ground-glass sockets in the cover, through which the electrodes, the gas inlet tube, and the tip of the buret can be introduced. The vessel may be fitted with an outlet controlled by a tap, through which the solution can be removed when the titration is complete. In this case the solution is stirred by the protective gas, which is blown in tangentially. Mechanical stirring (generally magnetic) is more effective.

The protective gas, which is usually nitrogen, should be purified for safety by passage through a soda lime or potassium hydroxide tower, since even very small carbon dioxide contents can interfere because of the large quantities of protective gas used and its intimate contact with the solution.

Burets (5- or 10-ml) with automatic zero-point adjustment are used. Alkaline titrant solutions are best stored in polyethylene vessels, since this improves the constancy of their titer (304).

The neck of the vessel should be slightly narrower than the ground-glass adapter of the buret which can then be fitted directly owing to the flexibility of the plastic. The buret is fitted with soda lime tubes to purify the incoming air.

Syringe pump burets are preferable to ordinary burets. A 1-ml syringe buret is particularly useful, since this allows the use of concentrated titrant solutions and so avoids excessive dilution of the reaction solution. This is particularly important in the case of alkaline solutions containing alcohol.

b. Special Notes on Ultramicrotitrations

α. *Potentiometric End-Point Detection.* The determination may be carried out either in a microbeaker (diameter about 1 cm) with immersed glass and reference electrodes (303) (or micro single rod measuring cell) and a magnetic stirrer, or in a bowl glass electrode. In the latter case the wall of the vessel forms the membrane of the glass electrode. The reference electrode may be separate, or the bowl glass electrode is fitted with a reference electrode. The solution is stirred by a vibration stirrer or by a stream of protective gas bubbled in tangentially.

β. *End-Point Detection with Indicators.* The titration is carried out in a microbeaker. If a protective gas is to be used, the beaker is placed in a container, which is flushed with the gas (Fig. 72) (305).

γ. *Burets.* Syringe pump burets are used in most cases. The plunger material may be glass, Teflon, or mercury, and the plunger is driven via a micrometer screw. The buret tip (which is sometimes made of polyethylene) dips into the solution, and the titrant solution can be measured out with an accuracy of a fraction of a microliter. In connection with errors due to evaporation, see Chapter 5, Section IX,1.

c. Procedures

Micro Determination of Amines (304, 306, 307)

Reagents and Apparatus:
   Glacial acetic acid, anal. grade
   Benzene, chlorobenzene, or chloroform
   0.01 *N* perchloric acid in dioxane (0.85 ml of 72% perchloric acid is
      dissolved in 1 liter of dioxane. The solution is standardized against
      potassium biphthalate.)
   Crystal violet, 0.1% in glacial acetic acid
   Glass and calomel electrodes
   Measuring instrument or recorder

Procedure: The substance (5 to 10 mg) (approximately 0.05 to 0.1 meq) is dissolved in 10 ml of glacial acetic acid; 30 ml of chloroform are added, and the solution is titrated potentiometrically. For titration with indicators, the sample is dissolved in a little glacial acetic acid and diluted with about 20 ml of an inert solvent; a little indicator is then added, and the solution is titrated to a clear blue tint. Blank titers must be taken into account.

Polar aprotic solvents may also be used instead of the solvents mentioned above.

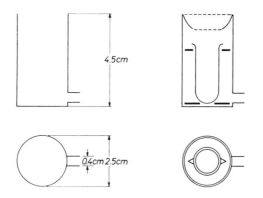

FIG. 72. Experimental arrangement for ultramicro titrations in the absence of air. A beaker is fixed in a chamber (dimensions as shown) by means of suitable plastic inserts. The funnel-shaped insert in the upper part of the chamber prevents air from diffusing in. The flushing gas (nitrogen purified with soda asbestos) is introduced under a pressure of from 50 to 150 mm Hg above atmospheric pressure. The solution is stirred magnetically. [Belcher *et al.* (305).]

Microdetermination of Acids. The quantities used are as for the microdetermination of amines, and the titration is carried out with 0.01 *N* alkali solution. The other conditions are as in the procedures for macro-determinations. Since very dilute titrant solutions are used, the titration of very weak acids (phenols) is difficult, and can only be achieved by potentiometric methods. Blank titers must be taken into account.

2. REACTIONS OF LEWIS ACIDS WITH LEWIS BASES

a. General

As was pointed out in the theoretical introduction, there are some reactions that undeniably possess a typical neutralization character, but which cannot involve protons (or their solvates). These are reactions of compounds that can accept electron pairs (Lewis acids) with compounds that can donate electron pairs (Lewis bases). We therefore refer to these compounds as (electron) acceptors and (electron) donors.

Typical acceptors are the halides of the third and fourth subgroups of the periodic system, as well as tin tetrachloride, antimony penta-chloride, and ferric chloride. Typical donors are tertiary amines of various natures (primary and secondary amines give side reactions, and so are not used) and compounds containing oxygen, particularly ethers.

The two classes of compounds generally react stoichiometrically with one another in the ratio 1:1, though some exceptions are known. Since these reactions are only occasionally used for analytical purposes, they will be described only briefly.

b. Solvents

Inert solvents such as hydrocarbons are mostly poor solvents for the acceptors, and even worse for the adducts formed. They are therefore rarely used. The usual solvents are aprotic, but "waterlike" solvents (308), generally acid chlorides and similar compounds, including thionyl chloride, sulfuryl chloride, phosphorus oxychloride, acetyl chloride, arsenic trichloride, benzoyl chloride, and acetic anhydride.*

These compounds have a small intrinsic conductance, which suggests that they undergo a dissociation similar to that of water (but aprotic).

In addition to these compounds, it is sometimes possible to use other polar substances, such as nitrobenzene and acetonitrile.

c. End-Point Detection

Potentiometric indication is very rarely used. However, a platinum electrode combined with a reference electrode of the second kind has been described, the electrolyte used being a solution of tetramethylammonium chloride in thionyl chloride. This system is claimed to give sharp end points even in very dilute solutions (0.001 N !) (309).

Good results are obtained with indicators, generally crystal violet; benzanthrone (310) can also be used. This is the most convenient method of end-point detection.

The most important physical method is the conductivity method, which has been used in the great majority of cases (particularly in earlier work). There is little difference in procedure between this and the ordinary conductometric methods, but instead of the usual ac resistance measurement (Wheatstone bridge), an ohmmeter (dc) is used for solutions with very low conductivities (311).

Other very nonspecific procedures with very wide applicability have recently been described. These include thermometric indication (312, 313) (see Chapter 2, Section V) and indication by measurement of the dielectric constant (314). The high-frequency method (Chapter 2, Section IV) can also be used.

---

*Liquefied gases such as SO_2 and NH_3 are seldom used in analysis, and are therefore not discussed.

d. Practical Applications

α. Titration of Donors (Lewis Bases). *N*-Heterocycles such as pyridine in thionyl chloride and nitrobenzene have been titrated conductometrically with boron tribromide (315, 316). High-frequency and potentiometric methods can also be used (309, 317). These bases can also be titrated with tin or titanium tetrachloride and with benzanthrone as the indicator in phosphorus oxychloride, sulfuryl chloride, and thionyl chloride (310).

An interesting method is the spectrophotometric end-point detection in the direct titration of aromatic hydrocarbons (e.g., naphthalene) with tetracyanoethylene (318). They form colored π complexes in chloroform with the hydrocarbons, which act as donors. Owing to the different basicities of the hydrocarbons, they can even be determined in the presence of one another (Fig. 73).

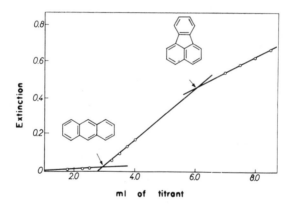

FIG. 73. Spectrophotometric titration of anthracene and fluoranthene in chloroform with 0.1 *N* tetracyanoethylene. [Schenk and Ozolins (318).]

β. Titration of Acceptors (Lewis Acids). A number of acceptors have been titrated in thionyl chloride with pyridine or quinoline, crystal violet being used as the indicator (319).

The chlorosilanes from trimethylchlorosilane to silicon tetrachloride have been titrated in acetonitrile, both potentiometrically and with indicators; the titrants used were 0.05 *N* phenazone and nitrone solutions (320).

The activities of catalysts (e.g., activated alumina) can be checked by automatic titration, as a slurry in acetonitrile, with butylamine. The height of the potentiometric break corresponds to the "acidity," while the quantity of titrant required is a measure of the surface area (321).

Trialkyl- and dialkylaluminum hydrides can be determined by conductometric or potentiometric titration with tertiary amines. Only the trialkylaluminums react with ethers (322). The determination may be carried out automatically (323). The end points can also be determined by measurement of the dielectric constant (314) or by enthalpy titrations (314).

3. CONDUCTOMETRIC TITRATIONS

a. Acids

Mineral acids have been titrated in glacial acetic acid with sodium acetate; N-shaped curves were obtained in the case of sulfuric acid (324). Similar effects were observed with organic dicarboxylic acids (325–327) on titration with tetrabutylammonium hydroxide in neutral or basic solvents; a detailed theoretical treatment is given in (326).

Phenols have also been titrated (328). Association effects in nonpolar solvents can be particularly clearly recognized by conductivity measurements (329).

b. Bases

Aliphatic amines have been titrated in benzene with trichloroacetic acid (330). The titration of diamines in alcohols with perchloric acid has been studied in detail by van Meurs and Dahmen (331).

A new method of conductometric determination makes use of acidic solvents (332). Weak bases (pK_B values 10 to 12) are partially protonated in a mixture of 340 ml of dioxane and 160 ml of pure formic acid. This gives a relatively high initial conductivity, and since (in contrast to other methods) the conductivity decreases at first on titration with 0.1 N perchloric acid, the curves obtained can be readily evaluated. Sharp separations can be obtained when bases with pK values in the appropriate range are titrated in the presence of one another, since a pK difference of only 1 is sufficient for separation in some cases. Stronger bases are leveled. The method appears to be capable of wider application if suitable solvent systems can be found for bases with other pK values (Fig. 74).

c. Sulfate

An interesting and important application of conductometric methods

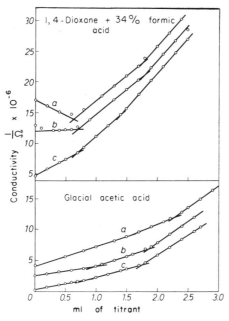

FIG. 74. Conductometric titrations of bases with 0.1 N perchloric acid in various solvents (for comparison): a, 8-hydroxyquinoline/anthranilic acid; b, p-bromoaniline/anthranilic acid; c, m-nitroaniline/anthranilic acid. Temperature = 0°C. [McCurdy and Galt (332).]

is the titration of sulfate in the presence of sulfonates. In aqueous solution, barium sulfate cannot be precipitated without coprecipitation of barium sulfonates. However, this coprecipitation does not occur in tetrahydrofuran. It is therefore possible to determine up to 0.5% (and even down to 0.1% in favorable cases) of sulfate in sulfonates by conductometric titration in tetrahydrofuran with barium acetate solution (333).

4. HIGH-FREQUENCY TITRATIONS

a. Amines

A number of publications (334–336) show that this method can be used for the titration of aromatic amines in glacial acetic acid with 0.1 N perchloric acid. As in conductometric titrations, the titrant solution is added in portions and the titration is evaluated graphically. The curve usually consists of linear branches forming an obtuse angle. This normal behavior may be disturbed if sparingly soluble salts precipitate out during the titration. It is then necessary to wait for a time before the final reading is taken (335).

The method can be used for bases up to a pK_B value of about 12 (p-nitroaniline). 2,4-Dinitroaniline can no longer be determined (336). In the case of aniline derivatives, a number of separations between two components have been described [e.g., p-bromoaniline and p-chloroaniline (!)]. The separation effect, which cannot as yet be explained in detail, appears to depend less on the difference in the pK values than on the difference between the molecular weights of the substances (336).

High-frequency titration can also be used for the determination of nitrates (by direct titration), hydrohalides (after addition of mercuric acetate), and phosphines (335). Alkaloids (nicotine, strychnine) have been determined by titration with picric acid (337). In this case the titration curve contains two discontinuities, the first corresponding to neutralization and the second to the formation of an adduct (π complex). The second discontinuity is the easier to evaluate.

b. Acids

Even very dilute solutions (down to 0.00025 M) of carboxylic acids in dimethylformamide have been titrated with 0.1 N sodium methoxide solution in benzene/methanol (338). The method can be used for the determination of acids with pK_A values of up to about 7. The angle in the curve at the end point may be acute or obtuse, depending on the nature of the acid.

Phenols and enols can also be titrated in ethylenediamine or in benzene/methanol (335, 339).

The influence of the titrant (340) and that of the solvent (341) on the sharpness of the end point have been systematically studied. Cesium methoxide was found to be the most suitable base, though potassium methoxide also gives good results. Sodium methoxide and lithium methoxide are less suitable. The best results were obtained in solvents with low basicities and high polarities (e.g., acetonitrile).

5. DETERMINATIONS BY VOLTAMMETRY

a. Amines

The conventional system of indicator and reference electrodes can be replaced by polarized platinum electrodes (for the principles of voltammetry, see Chapter 2, Section III), but the development of this method is still in its early stages (342). The choice of solvent is critical, since neither glacial acetic acid (Kolbe's hydrocarbon synthesis at the anode) nor aprotic solvents (addition of electrolytes to increase the conductivity has not been studied) can be used. The best solvent was found to be *m*-cresol, particularly in the form of a 1:1 mixture with acetonitrile. The titrant was a 0.1 *N* solution of perchloric acid in *m*-cresol.

A polarization current of 1 *μ*a gave potential curves with a very good maximum at the end point. The weakest base that could be determined was *p*-nitroaniline, which has a pK_B value of 12 (Fig. 75). Mixtures of strong and weak bases could not be accurately separated. For experimental details, see also ref. (343).

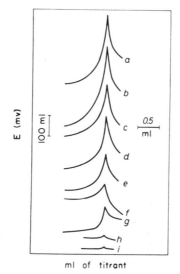

ml of titrant

FIG. 75. Polarovoltric titration of various bases in 1:1 acetonitrile/*m*-cresol with 0.1 *N* perchloric acid in *m*-cresol: *a*, diphenylguanidine; *b*, *n*-butylamine; *c*, benzylamine; *d*, diethylaniline; *e*, ethylaniline; *f*, aniline; *g*, 1-naphthylamine; *h*, *m*-nitroaniline; *i*, *p*-nitroaniline. [Svoboda (342).]

An interesting modification is the use of an internal indicator, such as diethylaniline (344) (as the perchlorate). A well-defined voltage maximum is obtained in the titration of this compound. Owing to its low basicity, therefore, it can be used as an indicator to show when neutralization is complete. Titrations have been carried out by this method in glacial acetic acid, acetonitrile, nitrobenzene, methyl isobutyl ketone, and methanol.

b. Acids

A number of acids ranging from benzoic acid to methyl salicylate have been determined in acetone and with tetrabutylammonium hydroxide as the titrant (343). The potential curve showed a more or less pronounced maximum at the end point, and this was followed by a steep drop.

The electrodes were two platinum wires, polarized by a current of 1 μa. A cheap tube voltmeter was used as the indicating instrument.

The accuracy of the end-point detection was at least equal to that of potentiometric titrations, but the method is less suitable for mixtures of acids having different strengths. However, a reliable result is obtained for the total acid content.

6. SPECTROPHOTOMETRIC DETERMINATIONS

a. Aromatic Amines

The main advantage of this method is the fact that it can be used for the separation of bases with small pK differences. A difference of only 1.5 pK units (345) (based on pK values measured in water) appears to be sufficient to permit a simultaneous determination, whereas a difference of 3 to 4 units is required in potentiometric titrations. Another advantage of the spectrophotometric method is the ease with which it can be adapted for microdeterminations. A 3.6×10^{-5} M solution of 5-nitro-1-naphthylamine in glacial acetic acid gave a satisfactory end point on titration with 0.05 N perchloric acid (345). The blank titer of the solvent is of considerable importance at these concentrations, but the example shows the value of the method.

One disadvantage is that something must be known in advance about the substances to be analyzed, in order that a suitable wavelength may be chosen. This is particularly important in simultaneous determinations, since it is generally necessary to change the wavelength during the titration in order to maintain optimum conditions (345).

The common aromatic amines become less intensely colored on conversion into the protonated form. A wavelength is therefore chosen at which the free amine absorbs light. The extinction then falls off to a minimum as the titration proceeds. The opposite behavior is shown by heterocyclic bases such as pyridine and quinoline.

Glacial acetic acid (345, 346) or acetonitrile (345) is used as the solvent, and the titrant is 0.5 N perchloric acid in glacial acetic acid (345) (to minimize dilution effects). Aliphatic bases can be determined sepa-

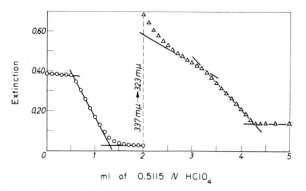

FIG. 76. Spectrophotometric titration of a mixture of 0.283 meq of di-*n*-butylamine, 0.409 meq of *N,N*-diethylaniline, 1.014 meq of aniline, and 0.509 meq of *o*-chloroaniline. The wavelength was changed during the titration. Solvent, acetonitrile; titrant, 0.511 *N* perchloric acid in glacial acetic acid. [Hummelstedt and Hume (345).]

rately in acetonitrile, since the arylamines act as internal indicators (Fig. 76).

Owing to the leveling action of glacial acetic acid, the only simultaneous determinations that are possible in this solvent are those of the very weakly basic chloro- and nitroarylamines (Fig. 77).

It is even possible, with the aid of a special procedure, to carry out a selective determination of primary and secondary arylamines (347). The titrant used in this case is a 0.001 *N* solution of acetic anhydride in pyridine. The sample is dissolved in pyridine that has been saturated with hydrogen chloride. Under these conditions the arylamines undergo almost instantaneous acetylation. The resulting acetyl derivatives absorb at lower wavelengths than the base, so that the extinction decreases as the titration proceeds. It is possible to obtain an accuracy of ±0.8% for a sample weighing from 1 to 8 mg. The determination is upset by water, but not by alcohols, aliphatic amines, or tertiary amines in general.

Primary aliphatic amines can be selectively determined by reaction with 2-ethylhexanal (348). In this case the titrant is colored (aldehyde group, absorption at 305 mμ). After the end point has been reached, the extinction increases, since the Schiff base formed by the aldehyde and the amine does not absorb in this region.

b. Phenols

Since phenoxide ions absorb at longer wavelengths than the corresponding phenols, direct spectrophotometric end-point detection is possible in the titration of phenols. A wavelength is chosen at which the phenol does not absorb (e.g., 329 mμ in the case of phenol itself). The extinction then rises to a maximum in the course of the titration.

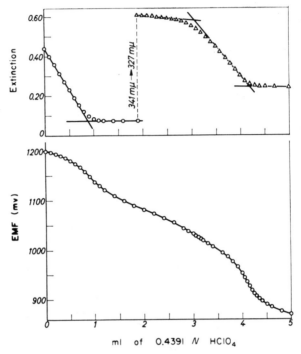

Fig. 77. Titration of a mixture of 0.407 meq of N,N-diethyl-p-chloroaniline, 0.951 meq of o-chloroaniline, and 0.506 meq of 2,5-dichloroaniline. Solvent, glacial acetic acid; titrant, 0.4391 N perchloric acid in glacial acetic acid. Top: spectrophotometric, with change of wavelength; bottom: potentiometric (glass and calomel electrodes). The superiority of the spectrophotometric method is obvious. [Hummelstedt and Hume (345).]

The solvents used were butylamine (349) and isopropanol (350), both of which have satisfactory optical properties. The titrants were a 0.05 N alcoholic potassium hydroxide solution (349) and a 0.4 N solution of tetrabutylammonium hydroxide in isopropanol (350). The quantities of sample used were about 0.1 and 1.0 meq, respectively, per 100 ml of solution. Accuracies of the order of $\pm1\%$ were obtained.

As is to be expected on theoretical grounds, the ability to distinguish between substances of different acidities is very good. However, since the pK values found in aqueous systems were no longer a good guide under other conditions, the possibility of a given separation could not be predicted. Nevertheless, the fundamental advantage of this method over potentiometric titrations was obvious. Thus m- and p-nitrophenols could be readily distinguished, and a mixture of diphenylphosphoric acid, 2,4-dinitrophenol, p-nitrophenol, and m-nitrophenol could be resolved by the use of different wavelengths.

One disadvantage in the case of phenols is the fact that the more strongly acidic members of this class also absorb at longer wavelengths. In the determination of weaker acids, therefore, the absolute optical transmission of the solution is greatly reduced.

7. COULOMETRIC DETERMINATIONS

Little work has been done as yet in this field. Factors that tend to oppose the general introduction of this method, apart from the need for extra electrical equipment, include:

(1) the conductivity of the solution must be fairly high;
(2) the addition of the required electrolyte (e.g., $NaClO_4$) to the titration solution has an adverse effect on the sharpness of the potentiometric break (in acidic media);
(3) it is difficult to obtain a current yield of 100% — this is the case, e.g., in the electrolysis of sodium perchlorate in glacial acetic acid/acetic anhydride; a platinum anode cannot be used, and it is necessary to use the much less convenient mercury anode [formation of Hg(I) acetate] (351);
(4) the usefulness of the method for the determination of acids is questionable, since an appreciable alkali error is to be expected because of the unavoidable use of a carrier electrolyte;
(5) oxidation is possible with a number of substances (e.g., aromatic amines).

The solvents used are glacial acetic acid/acetic anhydride (351) and acetonitrile (352, 353). The latter solvent was used with sodium or lithium perchlorate as the carrier electrolyte in the determination of a number of bases.

An interesting special case is the coulometric determination of water by the Karl Fischer method (354). This determination can be carried out automatically (355).

8. ANALYSIS OF MIXTURES OF CARBOXYLIC ACIDS, ACID
   ANHYDRIDES, ACID CHLORIDES, AND HYDROGEN CHLORIDE

a. Direct Determination of Carboxylic Acids in the Presence of Their Anhydrides

A carboxylic acid that is at least as strong as benzoic acid can be determined in a mixture with its anhydride by direct titration with a 2 N solution of triethylamine in benzene (356). The end point may be detected with the aid of color indicators (methyl red), in which case comparison solutions must be used. The end point can also be determined thermometrically. The reaction is nonstoichiometric. Potentiometric titration may be used for the systems phthalic acid/phthalic anhydride and maleic acid/maleic anhydride; the sample is dissolved in acetone, and the free α-dicarboxylic acid is titrated potentiometrically with a tertiary amine (357). Normal carboxylic acids do not interfere with the titration, since they are not sufficiently acidic. The more strongly acidic α-dicarboxylic acids are titrated as monobasic acids (Chapter 5, Section IX,8,c).

b. Determination of Carboxylic Acids and Acid Anhydrides in the Presence of One Another

The determination of these two components, though simple in theory, presents difficulties in practice, since the anhydrides differ greatly in reactivities. It is therefore difficult to give a method that can be used for the determination of all anhydrides.

The determination of anhydrides in general is based on their reaction with primary amines and alcohols (alkoxides).* The quantity of anhydride present can be calculated either from the quantity of amine used or from the difference between the quantity of acid in the product and that found on hydrolysis with water:

$$R'CO\text{---}O\text{---}OCR' + RNH_2 \rightarrow RNHCOOR' + R'COOH$$

$$R'CO\text{---}O\text{---}OCR' + H_2O \rightarrow 2\ R'COOH$$

The method that is actually used will depend on the circumstances, i.e., on the reactivity of the components and on their proportions. Thus the second method (based on the quantity of acid in the product) cannot be

---

*The anhydride could naturally be hydrolyzed with excess alkali. However, this procedure is very inaccurate, owing to the small difference in equivalent weight between the anhydride and the acid. It is also nonspecific

used for the determination of small quantities of anhydride in the presence of large quantities of carboxylic acid, since a relatively large error is unavoidable (difference between two large numbers).

An important point is the reactivity of the amine with which the sample is treated. The most active is aniline. In the case of very reactive carboxylic acids (e.g., acetic acid), however, there is a danger that the free acid will cause acylation as well as the anhydride. Less reactive amines such as m-nitroaniline or m-chloroaniline should therefore be used for these acids. To obtain quantitative reactions with amines that react sluggishly, the acylation should be carried out in the presence of glacial acetic acid (salt formation); good results have been obtained by this method for twenty different anhydrides (358). A solution in glacial acetic acid/benzene is kept at 70°C for from 3 minutes to 1 hour, depending on the reactivity of the anhydride; the unreacted m-chloroaniline is then back-titrated with sodium nitrite (diazotization).

α. *Determination of Anhydrides of α-Dicarboxylic Acids (359)*

Principle: The anhydride is allowed to react with excess aniline in acetone:

$$R \underset{CO}{\overset{CO}{<}} O \; + \; C_6H_5-NH_2 \; - \; R \underset{COOH}{\overset{CO-NH-C_6H_5}{<}}$$

The anilinic acid formed in the reaction is titrated with alkali. If free dicarboxylic acid is present, the value obtained (anilinic acid number) is correspondingly increased, since the acid does not react with the aniline. The content of free acid can be calculated from the difference. At low acid contents, it is better to determine the free acid content directly (see Chapter 5, Section IX,8,c). If yet other components are present, an hydrolysis value is also required for the calculation.

Determination of the Anilinic Acid Number

Reagents:
Acetone, anhydrous, neutral
Aniline, distilled
0.5 N alcoholic potassium hydroxide solution
Phenolphthalein

Procedure: The anhydride (3 to 7 mmoles) is dissolved in about

10 ml of acetone; 5 ml of aniline are added, and the solution is mixed well and titrated with 0.5 N alkali solution, in the presence of phenolphthalein. No interference is caused by any anilinic acid which may precipitate.

This method has been used for the determination of phthalic anhydride, tetrachlorophthalic anhydride, succinic anhydride, maleic anhydride, and the maleic acid/linseed oil adduct.

Determination of Total Acid
(Free Carboxylic Acid and Hydrolyzed Anhydride)

Instead of the normal hydrolysis value determination (360), the sample may be dissolved in about 10 ml of pyridine, and, after gradual dilution with 20 to 30 ml of water, titrated with 0.5 N aqueous potassium hydroxide in the presence of phenolphthalein (used for phthalic anhydride). The hydrolysis of the anhydride is catalyzed by pyridine. Ester is not included in the result. A blank titer should be taken into account if necessary.

β. Potentiometric Determination of Acetic and Propionic Anhydrides

Principle: The anhydride is treated with excess *m*-nitroaniline. The excess of the amine is back-titrated potentiometrically (360a). The method is particularly recommended for small anhydride contents, since large samples can be used. It is a variant of another method which involves bromometric titration of *m*-nitroaniline (361).

Reagents and Apparatus:
   Glacial acetic acid, anhydrous
   0.1 N perchloric acid in dioxane or glacial acetic acid
   0.1 N *m*-nitroaniline in glacial acetic acid; 3.5 gm of the amine are dissolved in 250 ml of anhydrous acetic acid
   Glass and calomel electrodes
   Measuring instrument or recorder

Procedure: The sample, which should contain from 50 to 150 mg of anhydride, is dissolved in 30 ml of glacial acetic acid; 20.0 ml of nitroaniline solution are added, and the vessel is closed and left to stand for 30 minutes; 50 ml of glacial acetic acid are then added and the titration to the first potentiometric break is carried out in the usual manner.

To standardize the nitroaniline solution, 20.0 ml are diluted with 80 ml of glacial acetic acid and titrated in the same way. The difference between the two determinations corresponds to the anhydride content (1 ml of 0.1 N perchloric acid $\equiv$ 10.2 mg of acetic anhydride or 13.0 mg of propionic anhydride).

Siggia and Hanna (362) have described a similar method based on the reaction with aniline in the absence of solvents and back-titration with 0.2 N hydrochloric acid in glycol/isopropanol (G-H mixture); the end point is determined potentiometrically. The reaction times are given in Table 14.

TABLE 14

REACTIVITIES OF ANHYDRIDES OF CARBOXYLIC ACIDS

Compound	Minutes	Temperature
Acetic anhydride	5	Room temperature
Propionic anhydride	5	Room temperature
Butyric anhydride	5	Room temperature
Maleic anhydride	15	Room temperature
Phthalic anhydride	15	100°C
Camphanic anhydride	45	100°C

A better method appears to be by reaction with a 0.5 N solution of morpholine in methanol at room temperature. After a reaction time of 5 minutes, the excess base is back-titrated with 0.5 N hydrochloric acid in methanol in the presence of dimethyl yellow/methylene blue (363).

γ. *Determination of Anhydrides and Acids in the Presence of One Another, with Indicators (364)* [For Micro Method see ref. (360)]

Principle: The anhydride is reacted with water on the one hand, and with sodium alkoxide on the other:

$$RCO\text{—}O\text{—}OCR + H_2O \rightarrow 2\ RCOOH$$

$$RCO\text{—}O\text{—}OCR + NaOR' \rightarrow RCOONa + RCOOR'$$

Hydrolysis with water yields 2 moles of acid per mole of anhydride, whereas the reaction with alkoxide gives 1 mole of acid (or salt) and 1 mole of ester. The acid formed is determined alkalimetrically. The difference between the two titrations corresponds to the anhydride content.

Reagents:

Dioxane, anhydrous, anal. grade

Pyridine, anal. grade, distilled

0.1 *N* sodium methoxide solution in a 1:4 methanol/benzene mixture (standardized against benzoic acid with thymol blue as the indicator)

0.1 *N* trimethylbenzylammonium hydroxide (Triton B) (50 ml of the commercial 30% aqueous solution are made up to 1 liter with pyridine. If any turbidity develops, it is discharged by the addition of water. The solution is standardized against benzoic acid in alcohol.)

Thymol blue, 0.2% in dioxane

Sample: The substance (50 to 100 mg) is dissolved in dioxane and made up to 10 ml to form the stock solution. Alternatively, each sample may be weighed out separately. Care should be taken to exclude water vapor.

Total Acid after Hydrolysis with Water

The stock solution (2.0 ml) is placed in a 25-ml Erlenmeyer flask, 1 ml of pyridine and 0.1 ml of water are added, and the mixture is heated on a steam bath for 1 to 10 minutes, depending on the reactivity of the anhydride. 10 ml of pyridine and 1 to 3 drops of indicator are added, and the solution is titrated with Triton B until the color changes to blue (titer A); carbon dioxide is excluded during the titration.

Acid after Hydrolysis with Alkoxide

The stock solution (2.0 ml) containing 1 to 3 drops of indicator is titrated with 0.1 *N* sodium methoxide solution until the color changes to blue (titer B).

Calculation: The difference between titers A and B corresponds to the anhydride content (1 ml ≡ 0.1 mmole of anhydride). The content of free acid is calculated from 2B−A.

This method has been used for the determination of acetic anhydride, propionic anhydride, butyric anhydride, benzoic anhydride, succinic anhydride, maleic anhydride, and phthalic anhydride.

The determination is upset by readily hydrolyzable esters (e.g., formates and certain lactones).

c. Determination of Carboxylic Acids, Acid Chlorides, and Free Acids in the Presence of One Another

Analyses of this nature are important for the assessment of the purity of acid chlorides. Free hydrogen chloride can be readily determined by potentiometric titration with a tertiary base (365). Interference may occur if α-dicarboxylic acids are present, since these are sufficiently acidic to be included in the determination.

For the determination of hydrochloric acid, the sample is treated with m-chloroaniline (365) or with alcohol (364):

$$RCOCl + Cl—C_6H_4—NH_2 \rightarrow R—CO—NH—C_6H_4—Cl + HCl$$

$$RCOCl + C_2H_5OH \rightarrow RCOOC_2H_5 + HCl$$

The hydrochloric acid liberated can be titrated either potentiometrically (365) with aqueous NaOH, or against thymol blue (color change from red to yellow) with sodium methoxide solution (364). Any free carboxylic acid present can also be determined by further titration.

If free carboxylic acids are not to be determined, the total hydrogen chloride and acid chloride can be determined by direct potentiometric titration with 0.5 N cyclohexylamine in tetrahydrofuran (366).

The reaction

$$RCOCl + 2\ C_6H_{11}NH_2 \rightarrow RCO—NHC_6H_{11} + C_6H_{11}NH_2 \cdot HCl$$

takes place almost instantaneously, so that the titration need not be carried out slowly except in the neighborhood of the end point. Carboxylic acids (except α-dicarboxylic acids) do not interfere. The content of free hydrogen chloride must be determined separately.

Strict exclusion of atmospheric moisture is even more important in the determination of acid chlorides than in the case of anhydrides. Liquids are best sealed inside glass spheres for weighing.

Potentiometric Determination of Hydrogen Chloride in the Presence of Carboxylic Acids and Acid Chlorides (365)

Reagents and Apparatus:
    Ether, anhydrous
    Chlorobenzene, anhydrous
    0.1 N tripropylamine in chlorobenzene, standardized against maleic
        acid (monobasic in this case!)
    Glass and calomel electrodes
    Measuring instrument or recorder

Procedure: The sample, which should contain not more than 1 mmole of hydrogen chloride, is dissolved in 1:1 mixture of ether and chlorobenzene and titrated potentiometrically in the usual manner.

Notes: The determination of hydrogen chloride can also be carried out in dioxane with thymol blue as indicator (red-yellow color change) (364). Tributylamine (364) or *N*-dimethylcyclohexylamine may be used instead of tripropylamine. α-Dicarboxylic acids are determined potentiometrically in acetone in a similar manner (357).

Determination of Acid Chlorides and Free Carboxylic Acid in the Presence of One Another (365)

Reagents and Apparatus:
   m-Chloroaniline, freshly distilled
   0.5 *N* sodium hydroxide solution
   0.1 *N* sodium hydroxide solution
   Glass and calomel electrodes
   Measuring instrument or recorder

Procedure: Approximately 10 meq of the acid chloride are weighed and dissolved in a mixture of 25 ml of acetone and 5 ml of *m*-chloroaniline in a 250-ml Erlenmeyer flask with a ground-glass neck. The flask is stoppered and shaken well, with cooling. After a reaction time of 5 minutes, 5 ml of water are added, and the mixture is shaken well to dissolve the hydrochlorides that have precipitated out. The solution is then washed into a beaker with acetone.

Most of the acid present is neutralized with a measured quantity of 0.5 *N* sodium hydroxide solution (to pH 4). The remainder of the acid is then titrated with 0.1 *N* sodium hydroxide solution. The first potentiometric break occurs between pH 5 and pH 6, and corresponds to the hydrochloric acid present (that formed from acid chloride together with free hydrogen chloride). The second break, between pH 8 and pH 9.5, is a measure of the free carboxylic acid present. Free hydrogen chloride must be determined separately and subtracted from the first titer to find the content of free acid chloride.

Note: The sharpness of the first potentiometric break increases with decreasing dielectric constant of the solvent mixture, since the acid is the positively charged chloroanilinium ion. Consequently the water content must not be too high. It could be advantageous to use alcoholic alkali solutions.

9. Pharmaceutical Products

Very many analyses of pharmaceutical products have been described, so that only a general survey of the field can be given here (367).

a. Bases

In addition to the common amines, this group includes the alkaloids, basic sulfonamides, antihistamines, antibiotics, narcotics, oxazolines, pyrazolones, quaternary ammonium compounds, and amino acids.

Since these compounds are generally present as their hydrochlorides, it is necessary either to carry out the acidimetric determination after addition of mercuric acetate (see Chapter 5, Section IV,1,b) or to make the aqueous solution alkaline and extract the free base with solvents. Compounds determined by these methods and titration with perchloric acid include papaverine hydrochloride, morphine hydrochloride, prostigmine hydrobromide, deoxyephedrine hydrochloride, and histidine hydrochloride (368, 369). Morphine and codeine in the same sample can be determined by a total base titration with perchloric acid, and an alkalimetric determination of the morphine (as an acid) (370).

Tomicek (371) has titrated basic sulfonamides. A number of alkaloids have been determined by photometric titration with malachite green as the indicator (372). The antibiotic Nystatin has been titrated potentiometrically in glacial acetic acid (373). High-frequency titration has also been used. The titrant was picric acid, and different bases (nicotine, strychnine) gave curves with two discontinuities (337). An interesting determination is that of N-glycosides in the presence of amines by potentiometric titration in aprotic solvents (374). Purine bases such as caffeine and theophylline can be determined in nitromethane after addition of acetic anhydride (375). The analysis of narcotics has been reported by Levi and Farmilo (376, 377). If basic impurities (excipients) are present (e.g., magnesium or calcium stearate in tablets), the base to be determined may be extracted (378), or if it is present as the hydrochloride, it may be determined directly by addition of mercury acetate after neutralization of the basic impurities. If emulsification occurs during the extraction, anti-foaming agents such as capryl alcohol or silicone defoamer may be added.

Any water present may be eliminated by addition of acetic anhydride *(time must be allowed for this reaction),* provided that no primary or secondary amines are to be included in the determination.

b. Acids

In addition to carboxylic acids and amino acids, this group includes the sulfonamides (Chapter 5, Section VIII,4), the barbiturates (Chapter 5, Section VIII,2), and the phenols (Chapter 5, Section VI,2). These determinations need not be discussed in detail, but a few special determinations are interesting. Thus salts of barbiturates can be determined by dissolution in dimethylformamide, passage through an acidic cation exchanger, and alkalimetric determination of the eluate (379). Barbituric acid can be determined in pyridine by addition of a neutral solution of silver nitrate and titration of the acid liberated [thymol blue, blank titer must be determined (380)] (see also Chapter 5, Section VIII,12). The analysis of p-aminosalicylic acid and its sodium salt by two extractions with either acetone or methanol and acidimetric titration against thymol blue has been described by Chatten (381). The optimum conditions for the determination of barbiturates are reported by Stainier (382).

10. DETERMINATION OF BASES AND ACIDS IN HYDROCARBONS

a. Bases

Amines can have a serious effect on the efficiency of cracking catalysts. Their determination in petroleum products is therefore important.

The ASTM specification D 664 describes the potentiometric determination of bases in benzene/isopropanol/water 500:495:5. The titrant is 0.1 N alcoholic hydrochloric acid, and the titration is carried out to the potentiometric break, or, when no break is observed, to the pH of a buffer system consisting of collidine/hydrochloric acid in the same solvent. The titration includes bases with pK_B values of less than 9 (based on water as the solvent). Wittmann (383) used potentiometric titration in glacial acetic acid with perchloric acid for the determination of the basic amines in diesel oil and in the middle oil obtained by hydrogenation of coal. Basic nitrogen contents of down to about 1 ppm could be determined with 0.01 N perchloric acid in glacial acetic acid (error ±0.2 ppm of nitrogen). Since up to 100 ml of oil was required, homogeneous solutions in glacial acetic acid could not be obtained. However, no difficulties were encountered in the titration of the well-stirred suspension.

If acetic anhydride is used instead of glacial acetic acid, tertiary amines can be determined selectively. There is again no interference as a result of the formation of two phases (384).

To avoid titration in a two-phase system, a 1:1 mixture of benzene and glacial acetic acid (385) or chlorobenzene and glacial acetic acid (386) may be used. Chlorobenzene is better for potentiometric titrations, since it has less effect on the conductivity of the solution than benzene. Methyl violet is used as an indicator for the titration in benzene/glacial acetic acid (385).

Strongly basic and weakly basic amines can be distinguished by potentiometric titration in chlorobenzene with 0.1 N hydrochloric acid in isopropanol (386). It is probably better, however, to use polar aprotic solvents with 0.1 N perchloric acid in dioxane. Methyl isobutyl ketone has been used for titrations of this type (387).

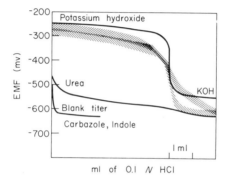

FIG. 78. Potentiometric titration of various bases in 1:1 glacial acetic acid/chlorobenzene with 0.1 N perchloric acid.   ▨▨▨ Crude oil, shale oil, and petroleum distillate and residue.   ▧▧▧ Pyridine, ammonium hydroxide, butylamine, 3,5-dimethylpyridine, acridine, 3-methylpyridine, quinoline, pyridine. [Deal *et al.* (386).]

Pyrrole and diphenylamine derivatives are not included in the titration, since they are not sufficiently basic (386). Depending on the nature of the sample, this nonbasic nitrogen accounts for between 40 and 80% of the total nitrogen (386). Since it also depends on the method used for the determination, data on the amine contents of hydrocarbons are meaningless unless the method is stated. The best solvent for the determination of very weak bases is probably chlorobenzene/glacial acetic acid, since this system has the lowest basicity (Fig. 78). Methyl isobutyl ketone is less suitable, but has the advantage that it does not cause leveling. Systems containing alcohols give particularly poor potential curves owing to the relatively high basicities of the alcohols, and the results obtained for the amine content are too low.

b. Acids

The determination of acids in hydrocarbons, and particularly in lubricants, is often important because of the corrosive action of these compounds. The DIN specification 53658 describes the determination of the acid value, which is the number of milligrams of potassium hydroxide required for neutralization of 1 gm of oil. In this determination, 2 to 10 gm of oil are dissolved in a 2:3 benzene/alcohol mixture saturated with the indicator alkali blue, and the solution is titrated with 0.1 N alcoholic potassium hydroxide solution until the color changes to red.

ASTM specification D 664 describes a potentiometric method in which isopropanol is used instead of ethanol (see Chapter 5, Section IX,10,a). The titration is carried out to the potentiometric break. The potential is checked by means of a buffer system (m-nitrophenol/KOH) in the same solvent mixture. This also provides a reference point to which the titration can be taken if no potentiometric break is observed. ASTM D974 describes the use of α-naphtholbenzein for the detection of the end point.

The method would probably be improved by the use of quaternary ammonium bases as titrants in aprotic solvents.

11. Determination of Mercaptans and Disulfides, Particularly in Hydrocarbons

The best and easiest method for the determination of mercaptans is by iodometry (388). Bromometric methods, which also permit the determination of disulfides (389), are also known.

Owing to lack of specificity, however, these methods and the alkalimetric method (Chapter 5, Section VIII,11) cannot be used for the determination of small quantities of mercaptan in the presence of large quantities of other substances. A very important practical example is the determination of mercaptans in hydrocarbons, where the quantities present are usually very low (in the ppm range).

The best methods for analyses of these type are titrations with salts of heavy metals (copper, mercury, or silver). The end point may be found potentiometrically, amperometrically, or with color indicators.

No interference is caused by disulfides, which are readily formed from mercaptans in the presence of oxidizing agents (including atmospheric oxygen). These can also be determined after reduction to mercaptans.

a. Titrations with Copper Salts

The reagent used is the alcohol-soluble copper oleate or, better, copper butyl phthalate (390). The reaction leads to reduction of the bivalent copper:

$$4 \text{ RSH} + 2 \text{ Cu}^{++} \longrightarrow 2 \text{ CuSR} + \text{RS} - \text{SR} + 4 \text{ H}^+$$

The end point is recognized from the blue color produced by excess copper ions. Owing to the low color intensity of these ions, however, the method is not very sensitive (only 0.1 N solutions can be used). The sharpness of the end-point detection can be improved by a factor of 10 by the addition of diphenylcarbazone as an indicator (390a). Butanol must be used as the solvent in this case, since the indicator does not respond to copper ions in aqueous solution. The titration can also be carried out potentiometrically with a platinum indicator electrode (390a).

It should be noted that the determination is subject to interference by halide ions, since the dissociation of the copper halides is evidently largely suppressed in the nonpolar medium.

Little use is made of titrations with copper salts for this purpose.

b. Titrations with Mercury Salts

Mercury salts (acetate, nitrate, perchlorate) are very useful for the analysis of mercaptans, owing to the ease of end-point detection with color indicators. Either diphenylcarbazone (391) or Michler's thioketone (392) is used as the indicator. The end point may also be determined potentiometrically with a mercury electrode.

Mixed thioethers having the general formula $(C_6H_5)_3$ C—S—Ar react with mercury ions, and can therefore also be determined (391). Interference is caused by hydrogen sulfide (which is included in the determination) and by halide ions. The presence of large quantities of olefins is also undesirable owing to the possibility of addition of mercury salts to double bonds.

c. Titrations with Silver Salts

This is the best method for the titration of mercaptans, particularly in trace determinations The end point is found either amperometrically with a rotating platinum electrode (393) or potentiometrically (394), the latter being particularly advantageous. This is one of the most sensitive methods known, since extremely sharp potentiometric breaks are obtained even with 0.001 N silver nitrate solutions in alcoholic media.

The silver/silver sulfide electrode is used as the indicator electrode; it consists of an ordinary silver electrode, which is brought into contact with sodium sulfide solution (395). The calomel electrode is not recommended as the reference electrode, since chloride may pass into the reaction solution in some circumstances. The problem is solved by the use of an agar-agar/potassium nitrate bridge (395) or, better, a mercurous sulfate electrode. A glass electrode may also be used (396).

The solvent is a lower alcohol, preferably isopropanol, and the electrolyte is glacial acetic acid/sodium acetate, sodium acetate alone, or ammonia/sodium acetate (395). Sodium acetate alone may be regarded as the normal reagent. The ammonia prevents interference due to chloride ions (395) and the acetic acid prevents interference due to elementary sulfur (395, 397), which reacts with mercaptans in alkaline solution to form polysulfides; these behave in the same manner as hydrogen sulfide in forming salts with silver ions.

Hydrogen sulfide can, in principle, be determined in the presence of mercaptans, since its silver salt is much less soluble than those of the mercaptans (395, 398).

Two potentiometric breaks are therefore observed in the titration of a mixture, the first of which corresponds to the hydrogen sulfide. If elementary sulfur is also present, the situation becomes very complicated, and a simultaneous determination is not always possible (Fig. 79).

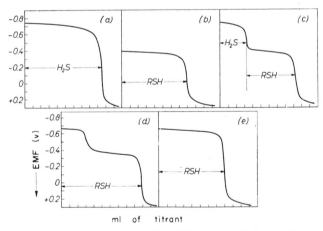

FIG. 79. Potentiometric titration of various SH compounds in 1:1 benzene/methanol (1.37% of sodium acetate) with alcoholic silver nitrate solution. Silver/silver sulfide electrode and calomel electrode with salt bridge. (a) Hydrogen sulfide; (b) n-amyl mercaptan; (c) hydrogen sulfide + n-amyl mercaptan; (d) n-amyl mercaptan + elementary sulfur (subequivalent); (e) n-amyl mercaptan + elementary sulfur (excess). [Karchmer (395).]

Removal of sulfur and hydrogen sulfide by agitation with mercury, as has been recommended, leads to loss of mercaptan (397, 399). The reader is referred to (395) for a description of the extremely complicated conditions prevailing in such systems.

Since mercaptans are oxidized by atmospheric oxygen, the use of a protective gas is recommended where great accuracy is requi.ed and in trace analyses.

Potentiometric Trace Determination of Mercaptans in Hydrocarbons (Particularly Gasolines)

Reagents and Apparatus:

Isopropanol, distilled over potassium hydroxide

Glacial acetic acid, saturated with sodium acetate, in a dropping bottle

0.001 *N* silver nitrate solution. (Preparation: 10.0 ml of 0.1 *N* silver nitrate solution are made up to 1 liter. The solution should aways be freshly prepared just before use.)

Silver/silver sulfide electrode (for preparation see above)

Mercurous sulfate electrode

Measuring instrument or recorder

Up to 40 gm of hydrocarbon, which should contain from 2 to 6 meq of mercaptan, are dissolved in about 60 ml of isopropanol. A few drops of the glacial acetic acid/sodium acetate solution are added and the titration is carried out to the potentiometric break (which is sharp) in the usual manner. If the determination is carried out rapidly with an automatic instrument, there is no need to exclude air; otherwise an atmosphere of nitrogen should be used.

One milliliter of 0.001 *N* silver nitrate solution corresponds to 32 μg of mercaptan S.

d. Determination of Disulfides

Disulfides can be relatively easily reduced to mercaptans and determined in this form. The only difficulty is that of carrying out the reduction accurately and quantitatively. The procedure used in most cases is reduction with zinc and acetic acid, which is subject to errors due to volatilization of lower mercaptans, incomplete reduction (particularly in the case of tertiary disulfides), and overreduction to hydrogen sulfide. The existing literature has been reviewed by Karchmer and Walker (400). A closed apparatus, which prevents losses during the reduction, is described. Satisfactory accuracy can be achieved in the case of primary and secondary disulfides, but the accuracy obtained in the determination of tertiary amines is only about 80 to 90%.

Stahl and Siggia (401) suggested the use of sodium borohydride as the reducing agent, but secondary and tertiary groups are not reduced by this reagent. The present author's experiments with sodium aluminum ethoxyethyl hydride gave good results with primary disulfides (no others were examined) since the reduction takes place instantaneously and a homogeneous system can be used. The excess of the reagent is destroyed by the addition of ethyl acetate followed by glacial acetic acid, and the solution is then diluted and titrated potentiometrically.

Any polysulfides or elementary sulfur present are reduced to hydrogen sulfide, which can be determined with the mercaptans (see Chapter 5, Section IX,11,c).

If any mercaptans are already present before the reduction, these can be determined and the result subtracted from the value found after reduction. Alternatively, they may be converted into thioethers by reaction with acrylonitrile (401a).

X. Calculations of the Results

If the equivalent weight of the substance to be determined is known, its concentration can be found from the formula:

$$\% = (V_x - V_b)N \times E \times 100/W$$

where V_x is the volume of titrant solution used in milliliters, V_b is the blank titer in milliliters, N is the normality of the titrant solution, E is the equivalent weight of the substance being determined, and W is the weight of the sample in milligrams.

If the equivalent weight is not known, or if it is desired to determine the total of a number of compounds, all of which contain the same functional groups, the calculation may be carried out by one of several methods, including the following:

1. CALCULATION OF THE EQUIVALENT WEIGHT

This calculation is useful in the analysis of mixtures of homologous compounds, since the result is the average equivalent weight:

$$E = W/(V_x - V_b)N$$

(For the meanings of the symbols, see preceding page.)

2. PERCENTAGE OF AN ELEMENT OR FUNCTIONAL GROUP CHARACTERIZING THE SUBSTANCE

In the determination of amines, it is useful to express the result as a percentage of nitrogen, so that the value obtained is directly related to any elementary analysis that may be carried out; moreover, subdivision into different types of amines becomes mathematically easy. The formula used is:

$$\% \text{ nitrogen} = (V_x - V_b)N \times \text{atomic weight of nitrogen}/W$$

(For the meanings of the symbols, see above.)

This type of calculation is not normally used in the case of oxygen functions such as carboxyl or phenolic hydroxyl groups, since the result may be ambiguous because of the different oxygen contents of the different groups. However, if errors of this nature can be ruled out, this type of calculation is quite useful. In the case of unknown compounds it is then simple, by a total oxygen determination, to set up an oxygen balance.

However, it is more usual in this case to calculate the result as a percentage of functional groups, particularly carboxyl groups (% COOH). This method has the disadvantage that recalculation is necessary before different values relating to the same substance can be compared. This is also true of comparative figures from elementary analyses.

3. CALCULATION OF THE NUMBER OF EQUIVALENTS PER GRAM, OR OF A MULTIPLE OF THIS NUMBER

In the case of the oxygen functions, this method has been built up into a system that permits the comparison of all data obtained and that is frequently used in fat analyses and in industry. The value found in the case of acids is the number of milligrams of potassium hydroxide required for neutralization of 1 gm of the substance. This quantity is known as the acid value:

$$\text{acid value (A.V.)} = (V_x - V_b)N \times 56,100/W$$

(For the meanings of the symbols, see above.)

It is possible in the same way to determine the saponification value, S.V., the ester value, E.V. (=S.V. − A.V.), and other data of this type.

These values are converted into the equivalent weight by means of the following formula:

$$E = 56,100/\text{A.V.}$$

PART III

Tables

TABLE I

ACIDIC AND BASIC STRENGTHS
OF VARIOUS COMPOUNDS IN AQUEOUS SOLUTION (402)

Note: The table is intended to provide an indication of the probable feasibility of the titration of various substances or classes of substances (cf. Chapter 5). It has therefore been made as comprehensive as possible. Where a given compound is not listed, it will generally be possible to find analogous compounds. Though the pK values given are not directly applicable to organic media, the values in these media will be largely proportional to the values in water. Small differences in pK are insignificant, partly because the values were determined by different methods, and so are not strictly comparable in many cases. This is particularly true of extreme values, which should generally be regarded as being only approximate.

TABLE I,1. INORGANIC ACIDS (403)

		pK_A			pK_A
H_3AsO_3	St 1	9.22	H_5IO_6	St 1	1.64
H_3AsO_4	St 1	2.32	NH_3		~23
	St 2	7	HN_3		4.67
	St 3	13	HNO_2		3.35
H_3BO_3	St 1	9.24	HNO_3		−1.32
$H_2B_4O_7$	St 1	~4	$H_2N_2O_2$	St 1	8.5
	St 2	~9	PH_4^+		~0
HBr		~−6	H_3PO_2		2.0
HOBr		8.68	H_3PO_3	St 1	1.80
$HBrO_3$		~0		St 2	6.16
HCN		9.40	H_3PO_4	St 1	1.96
HOCN		3.92		St 2	7.12
HSCN		~4		St 3	12.32
H_2CO_3	St 1[a]	6.52	$H_4P_2O_7$	St 1	0.85
	St 2	10.40		St 2	1.96
HCl		~−3		St 3	6.68
HClO		7.25		St 4	9.39
$HClO_2$		2	H_2S	St 1	6.9
$HClO_3$		~0		St 2	12.9
$HClO_4$		~−9	H_2SO_3	St 1[a]	1.96
H_2F^+		−6		St 2	7.0
HF		3.14	H_2SO_4	St 1	~−3
HI		~−8		St 2	1.92
HIO		10.6	$H_2S_2O_4$	St 1	0.35
HIO_3		0		St 2	2

[a] Dehydration.

215

TABLE I,2. ALIPHATIC CARBOXYLIC ACIDS

		pK_A				pK_A
a. *Monocarboxylic acids*				γ,δ-Hexenoic acid		4.76
Formic acid		3.75		δ,ϵ-Hexenoic acid		4.72
Acetic acid		4.73		Angelic acid		4.30
Propionic acid		4.87		Tiglic acid		5.00
n-Butyric acid		4.82		Propiolic acid		1.84
Isobutyric acid		4.81		Tetrolic acid		2.61
n-Valeric acid		4.79		d. *Hydroxy and keto acids*		
n-Caproic acid		4.84		Glycolic acid		3.82
Trimethylacetic acid		5.01		Lactic acid		3.86
b. *Dicarboxylic acids*				β-Hydroxybutyric acid		4.41
Oxalic acid	St 1	1.42		γ-Hydroxybutyric acid		4.71
	St 2	4.31		Glyceric acid		3.64
Malonic acid	St 1	2.79		d(l)-Tartaric acid	St 1	3.01
	St 2	5.68			St 2	4.16
Succinic acid	St 1	4.18		*meso*-Tartaric acid	St 1	3.22
	St 2	5.55		Dihydroxymaleic acid		1.15
Glutaric acid	St 1	4.33		Dihydroxyfumaric acid		1.10
	St 2	5.54		Glyoxalic acid		3.30
Adipic acid	St 1	4.41		Pyruvic acid		2.50
	St 2	5.28		Levulinic acid		4.59
Pimelic acid	St 1	4.50		δ-Ketovaleric acid		4.72
	St 2	5.40		Acetonedicarboxylic acid		3.10
Maleic acid	St 1	1.82		Diglycolic acid		2.96
	St 2	6.59		Citric acid	St 1	3.13
Fumaric acid	St 1	3.00			St 2	4.76
	St 2	4.52			St 3	6.40
Citraconic acid	St 1	2.29		e. *Halogenated acids*		
	St 2	6.15		Chloroacetic acid		2.81
Mesaconic acid	St 1	3.09		Dichloroacetic acid		1.30
	St 2	4.75		Trichloroacetic acid		0.70
Itaconic acid	St 1	3.85		α-Chlorobutyric acid		2.86
	St 2	5.45		β-Chlorobutyric acid		4.05
Acetylenedicarboxylic acid	St 1	1.75		γ-Chlorobutyric acid		4.50
	St 2	4.40		δ-Chlorovaleric acid		4.69
Oxalacetic acid	St 1	2.56		α-Chlorocrotonic acid		3.14
	St 2	4.37		β-Chlorocrotonic acid		3.84
c. *Unsaturated acids*				α-Chloroisocrotonic acid		2.80
Acrylic acid		4.26		β-Chloroisocrotonic acid		4.02
Crotonic acid		4.70		Bromoacetic acid		2.86
Isocrotonic acid		4.44		α,α-Dibromopropionic acid		1.48
Sorbic acid		4.77		α,β-Dibromopropionic acid		2.17
α,β-Hexenoic acid		4.72		α-Bromopropionic acid		2.97
β,γ-Hexenoic acid		4.58		β-Bromopropionic acid		4.01

TABLE I,2. *(Continued)*

		pK_A		pK_A
γ-Bromobutyric acid		4.58	*f. Others*	
Bromosuccinic acid	St 1	2.55	Cyanoacetic acid	2.43
	St 2	4.41	Thiocyanatoacetic acid	2.58
Dibromosuccinic acid	St 1	1.47	Isothiocyanatoacetic acid	6.62
	St 2	2.80	Nitroacetic acid	1.68
Iodoacetic acid		3.12	β-Nitropropionic acid	3.79
β-Iodopropionic acid		4.05	α-Sulfodipropionic acid	1.99
γ-Iodobutyric acid		4.64	β-Sulfodipropionic acid	3.62
Fluoroacetic acid		2.57	Thioglycolic acid	3.65
Trifluoroacetic acid		0.23	Thiodiglycolic acid	3.32
			Methylthioacetic acid	3.72

TABLE I,3. AROMATIC CARBOXYLIC ACIDS

		pK_A		pK_A
Benzoic acid		4.20	*o*-Benzoylbenzoic acid	3.43
o-Hydroxybenzoic acid	St 1	2.98	Sulfanilic acid	3.21
	St 2	13.00	2,3-Dihydroxybenzoic acid	2.94
m-Hydroxybenzoic acid		4.08	2,4-Dihydroxybenzoic acid	3.29
p-Hydroxybenzoic acid		4.54	2,5-Dihydroxybenzoic acid	2.97
o-Chlorobenzoic acid		2.89	2,6-Dihydroxybenzoic acid	1.30
m-Chlorobenzoic acid		3.81	3,4-Dihydroxybenzoic acid	4.48
p-Chlorobenzoic acid		4.03	3,5-Dihydroxybenzoic acid	4.04
o-Nitrobenzoic acid		2.20	3,5-Dinitrobenzoic acid	2.80
m-Nitrobenzoic acid		3.46	3,5-Diaminobenzoic acid	5.30
p-Nitrobenzoic acid		3.40	3,5-Dimethylbenzoic acid	4.32
o-Aminobenzoic acid		4.97	2,3-Hydroxymethylbenzoic acid	2.99
m-Aminobenzoic acid		4.79	2,4-Hydroxymethylbenzoic acid	3.17
p-Aminobenzoic acid		4.92	2,5-Hydroxymethylbenzoic acid	4.08
o-Toluic acid		3.90	2,6-Hydroxymethylbenzoic acid	2.98
m-Toluic acid		4.25	2,3-Chloronitrobenzoic acid	2.06
p-Toluic acid		4.37	2,4-Chloronitrobenzoic acid	2.00
m-Cyanobenzoic acid		3.70	2,5-Chloronitrobenzoic acid	2.21
p-Cyanobenzoic acid		3.51	4,2-Chloronitrobenzoic acid	2.00
o-Fluorobenzoic acid		3.27	4,3-Chloronitrobenzoic acid	3.34
m-Fluorobenzoic acid		3.85	3,2-Chloronitrobenzoic acid	2.36
p-Fluorobenzoic acid		4.14	3,6-Chloronitrobenzoic acid	1.85
o-Iodobenzoic acid		2.85	2,4,6-Tribromobenzoic acid	1.41
m-Iodobenzoic acid		3.80	Gallic acid	4.43
p-Iodobenzoic acid		3.93	2,4,6-Trihydroxybenzoic acid	1.68
Anisic acid		4.49	2,4,6-Trinitrobenzoic acid	0.65

TABLE I,3. *(Continued)*

		pK_A				pK_A
o-Phthalic acid	St 1	2.90	Trimellitic acid	St 1		2.50
	St 2	5.51		St 2		3.96
Isophthalic acid	St 1	3.54	Benzenehexacarboxylic acid	St 1		1.40
	St 2	4.62		St 2		2.19
Terephthalic acid	St 1	3.54		St 3		3.31
	St 2	4.46		St 4		4.78
4-Chlorophthalic acid		1.60		St 5		5.89
3,6-Dichlorophthalic acid		1.46		St 6		6.96
3-Nitrophthalic acid		1.88	Phenylacetic acid			4.31
4-Nitrophthalic acid		2.11	Cinnamic acid (*trans*)			4.43
o-Formylbenzoic acid		4.50	α-Phenylpropionic acid			4.38
Phthalamic acid		3.79	β-Phenylpropionic acid			4.64
Methyl o-phthalate		3.18	Mandelic acid			3.37
Methyl isophthalate		3.89	Benzilic acid			3.04
Nitroterephthalic acid		1.73	Hippuric acid			3.65
1-Methyl 2-nitroterephthalate		3.11	α-Naphthoic acid			3.70
4-Methyl 2-nitroterephthalate		1.82	β-Naphthoic acid			4.17

TABLE I,4. PHENOLS

	pK_A		pK_A
Phenol	9.95	2,4-Dichlorophenol	7.85
o-Cresol	10.20	2,4,6-Trichlorophenol	7.59
m-Cresol	10.01	2,4-Dinitrophenol	3.96
p-Cresol	10.17	2,5-Dinitrophenol	5.16
o-Chlorophenol	8.48	2,6-Dinitrophenol	3.58
m-Chlorophenol	9.02	3,4-Dinitrophenol	5.43
p-Chlorophenol	9.38	3,5-Dinitrophenol	6.68
o-Nitrophenol	7.23	Picric acid	0.71
m-Nitrophenol	8.35	α-Naphthol	9.85
p-Nitrophenol	7.14	β-Naphthol	9.93
m-Cyanophenol	8.61	Pyrocatechol	9.40
o-Aminophenol	9.95	Resorcinol	9.40
p-Aminophenol	10.68	Hydroquinone	10.00
m-Methoxyphenol	9.39	Pyrogallol	9.35
p-Methoxyphenol	10.16	Phloroglucinol	8.68

TABLE I.5. ENOLS

		pK_A
Methyl acetoacetate		10.70
Acetylacetone		8.16
Benzoylacetone		8.23
2-Methylhexanedione-3,5		9.43
2,2-Dimethylhexanedione-3,5		10.01
3-Methylpentanedione-2,4		10.87
3-Ethylpentanedione-2,4		11.34
Ascorbic acid	St 1	4.30
	St 2	11.82
Dimethylhydrorescorcinol		5.15
Triacetylmethane		5.81

TABLE I,6. HETEROCYCLES

	pK_A		pK_A
Allantoin	8.96	Methyluracil	9.52
Alloxan	6.64	Hydroxyuracil	8.64
Barbituric acid	4.00	Parabanic acid	6.92
Uric acid	5.82	Hydantoin	9.92
Caffeine	> 14	2-Furoic acid	3.16
Theobromine	8–10	3-Amidotetrazole	3.95
Theophylline	8.80	2-Thenoic acid	3.53
Xanthine	9.90	3-Thenoic acid	4.10
Violuric acid	4.57	2-Pyrrolecarboxylic acid	4.45

TABLE I,7. SPECIAL ACIDS

	pK_A		pK_A
Succinimide	9.62	Benzhydroxamic acid	6.52
Glutarimide	11.43	Saccharin	2.41
Phthalimide	9.90	Dipicrylamine	5.42
Cyanamide	9.40	Nitromethane	10.21
Dicyanimide	~ 1	Nitroethane	8.44
Dicyandiamide	14.22	Ethyl nitroacetate	5.85
Acetoxime	12.20	Nitrourea	4.15

TABLE I,7. *(Continued)*

	pK_A		pK_A
Nitromalonamide	3.24	Malonodinitrile	11.19
Thiophenol	6.50	Cyanoform	< 1
Benzyl mercaptan	9.43	Triethylsulfonylmethane	< 1
Methyl mercaptan	10.70	Benzenesulfinic acid	1.50
Methyl thioglycolate	7.68	Phenylboric acid	8.86
Diethyl malonate	13.30		

TABLE I,8. PEROXIDES

	pK_A
Hydrogen peroxide	11.60
Ethyl hydroperoxide	11.80
Isopropyl hydroperoxide	12.10
tert-Butyl hydroperoxide	12.80
Cumene hydroperoxide	12.60
Peracetic acid	8.20

TABLE I,9. EXTREMELY WEAK ACIDS

		pK_A		pK_A
Water	St 1	15.74	Trifluoroethanol	12.37
	St 2	~ 24	Trichloroethanol	12.24
Methanol		15.50	Acetamide	15.10
Ethanol		18.95	Diphenylamine	23
1-Propanol		19.33	Aniline	27
2-Propanol		21.05	Ammonia	33
Allyl alcohol		15.50	Triphenylmethane	33
Glycol		15.10	Diphenylmethane	35
Methyl glycol		14.80	Cymene	37
Propargyl alcohol		13.60		

TABLE I,10. Amino Acids (404)[a]

		pK_A			pK_A
Glycine	St 1	2.34	Histidine	St 1	1.82
	St 2	9.60		St 2	6.00 (Im)
Alanine	St 1	2.34		St 3	9.17 $(-NH_3^+)$
	St 2	9.69	Arginine	St 1	2.17
Valine	St 1	2.32		St 2	9.04 (NH_3^+)
	St 2	9.62		St 3	12.48 (Guan.)
Leucine	St 1	2.36	Ornithine	St 1	1.94
	St 2	9.60		St 2	8.65
Proline	St 1	1.99		St 3	10.76
	St 2	10.60	Lysine	St 1	2.18
Taurine	St 1	1.50		St 2	8.95 $(\alpha\text{-}NH_3^+)$
	St 2	8.74		St 3	10.53 $(\epsilon\text{-}NH_3^+)$
Tyrosine	St 1	2.20	Cystine	St 1	1.65 (COOH)
	St 2	9.11		St 2	2.26 (COOH)
	St 3	10.07 (OH)		St 3	7.85 (NH_3^+)
Diiodotyrosine	St 1	2.12		St 4	9.85 (NH_3^+)
	St 2	6.48 (OH!)	Glycylglycine	St 1	3.06
	St 3	7.82 $(NH_3^+!)$		St 2	8.13
Cysteine	St 1	1.96	β-Alanine	St 1	3.60
	St 2	8.18		St 2	10.19
	St 3	10.28 (SH)	ϵ-Amino-n-caproic		
Aspartic acid	St 1	1.88	acid	St 1	4.43
	St 2	3.65		St 2	10.75
	St 3	9.60			

[a] pK_A values of the fully protonated compounds (in the form $HOOC \ldots NH_3^+$).

TABLE I,11. Inorganic Bases[a]

		pK_A		pK_A
NH_3		4.75		
N_2H_4	St 1	5.89	Hg_2^{++}	9.00
	St 2	14.88	Hq^{++}	10.30
NH_2OH		8.03	Tl^{+++}	12.86
Mn^{++}		3.40	Li^+	−0.10
Cd^{++}		5.00	Mg^{++}	2.60
Co^{++}		5.10	Ca^{++}	1.30
Fe^{++}		3.50	Ba^{++}	0.60

[a] Metals as hydroxides or oxides.

TABLE I,12. Aliphatic and Cycloaliphatic Amines

	pK_B		pK_B
Ammonia	4.75	Ethanolamine	4.56
Methylamine	3.36	Diethanolamine	5.12
Ethylamine	3.33	Triethanolamine	6.23
n-Propylamine	3.42	Tris(hydroxymethyl)aminomethane	5.92
Isopropylamine	3.37	2-Cyanoethylamine	6.14
n-Butylamine	3.39	Di-2-cyanoethylamine	8.86
tert-Butylamine	3.55	Pyrrolidine	2.89
α-Dimethylethylamine	3.23	N-Methylpyrrolidine	3.83
Isoamylamine	3.40	Piperidine	2.80
Cyclohexylamine	3.36	N-Ethylpiperidine	3.59
Allylamine	4.24	Morpholine	5.48
Benzylamine	4.62	N-Methylmorpholine	6.87
Dimethylamine	3.30	Acetidine	2.71
Diethylamine	3.00	Aziridine	5.96
Trimethylamine	4.20	Cyclohexanonimine	4.85
Triethylamine	3.28	Diphenylketimine	7.18
Dimethylbenzylamine	4.98		

TABLE I,13. Aromatic Amines

	pK_B		pK_B
Aniline	9.42	m-Aminobenzoic acid	10.92
o-Toluidine	9.61	p-Aminobenzoic acid	11.64
m-Toluidine	9.31	Methyl o-aminobenzoate	11.82
p-Toluidine	8.93	Methyl m-aminobenzoate	10.36
o-Anisidine	9.51	Methyl p-aminobenzoate	11.54
m-Anisidine	9.80	p-Aminoazobenzene	11.02
p-Anisidine	8.71	Picramide	23.20
o-Nitroaniline	14.13	N-Methylaniline	9.15
m-Nitroaniline	11.40	N-tert-Butylaniline	6.90
p-Nitroaniline	12.00	Diphenylamine	13.12
m-Chloroaniline	10.44	N-Dimethylaniline	8.79
p-Chloroaniline	9.82	N-Dimethylpicramide	18.70
m-Bromoaniline	10.42	p-Nitrosodimethylaniline	9.72
p-Bromoaniline	10.00	α-Naphthylamine	10.08
o-Aminobenzoic acid	11.85	β-Naphthylamine	9.89

TABLE I,14. DIAMINES

		pK_B			pK_B
Ethylenediamine	St 1	3.91	trans-1,2-Diaminocyclohexane		
	St 2	7.00		St 1	4.06
1,4-Propylenediamine	St 1	3.38		St 2	7.53
	St 2	5.36	Piperazine	St 1	4.18
1,4-Diaminobutane	St 1	3.20		St 2	8.32
	St 2	4.65	Benzidine	St 1	9.30
1,8-Diaminooctane	St 1	3.00		St 2	10.37
	St 2	3.90	o-Phenylenediamine	St 1	9.53
cis-1,2-Diaminocyclohexane				St 2	> 12
	St 1	4.07	m-Phenylenediamine	St 1	9.12
	St 2	7.57		St 2	11.35
			p-Phenylenediamine	St 1	7.92
				St 2	10.71

TABLE I,15. HETEROCYCLES

	pK_B		pK_B
Pyridine	8.81	N-Methylpyrazole	10.45
2-Picoline	7.52	Pyrazine	13.40
3-Picoline	8.00	Thiazole	11.48
4-Picoline	8.00	Pyrrole	> 16
2-Methoxypyridine	10.72	Indole	> 16
3-Methoxypyridine	9.12	Carbazole	> 16
4-Methoxypyridine	7.38	Benzimidazole	8.47
2-Fluoropyridine	14.44	Imidazole	7.00
2-Chloropyridine	13.28	Pyrimidine	1.30
3-Chloropyridine	11.16	Triazole	11.40
2-Bromopyridine	13.10	Benzotriazole	12.40
2-Iodopyridine	12.18	Acridine	9.89
3-Acetylpyridine	10.82	Quinoline	8.94
3-Cyanopyridine	12.55	Isoquinoline	8.70
2-Aminopyridine	7.14	2-Hydroxyquinoline	14.30
3-Aminopyridine	8.02	3-Hydroxyquinoline	9.70
4-Aminopyridine	4.83	4-Hydroxyquinoline	11.70
Pyridine-N-oxide	13.21	5-Hydroxyquinoline	8.80
Collidine	6.69	Quinaldine	8.40
Pyrazole	11.51	Caffeine	13.39

TABLE I,15. *(Continued)*

		pK$_B$			pK$_B$
Theobromine		13.32	Quinidine	St 1	6.62
Theophylline		13.24		St 2	9.50
Xanthine		13.32	Brucine		3.10
Guanine		11.07	Strychnine	St 1	7.00
Cocaine		6.60		St 2	10.20
Quinine	St 1	6.66	Dimethylpyrone	.	13.70
	St 2	9.48			

TABLE I,16. SPECIAL BASES

	pK$_B$		pK$_B$
Acetamide	14.5	*O*-Methylisourea	4.28
Acetanilide	15.7	Methylurea	13.1
N-Methylacetanilide	14.5	Phenylurea	14.3
Acetamidine	1.70	Thiourea	15.0
Benzamidine	2.40	*S*-Methylisothiourea	4.17
Acetoxime	12.19	Acetyl hydrazide	10.76
Guanidine	0.50	Diethyl ether	17.59
N-Acetylguanidine	5.67	Dioxane	16.92
Diphenylguanidine	4.20	Acetone	21.2
Urea	13.80	Cyclohexanone	20.8

TABLE I,17. pK$_B$ VALUES OF PHOSPHINES[a]

R	pK$_B$	R	pK$_B$
Type R$_3$P		Type R$_2$PCH$_2$CH$_2$CN	
Cyclohexyl	4.30	Cyclohexyl	6.87
Methyl	5.35	2,4-Dimethylpentyl	7.19
Ethyl	5.31	Methyl	7.63
n-Propyl	5.36	*n*-Butyl	7.52
n-Butyl	5.57	*n*-Octyl	7.71
Isobutyl	6.03	2-Phenylethyl	10.57
n-Amyl	5.67		
2-*n*-Butoxyethyl	5.97		
2-Phenylethyl	7.40	Type RP(CH$_2$CH$_2$—CN)$_2$	
p-Methoxyphenyl	9.54	Methyl	10.39
2-Cyanoethyl	12.63	Ethyl	10.20
Phenyl	11.30	Phenyl	10.80

TABLE I,17. *(Continued)*

R	pK_B	R	pK_B
Type $R_2R'P$		Type R_2PH	
Dimethylethyl	5.39	Cyclohexyl	9.45
Diethylmethyl	5.39	n-Butyl	9.49
Dimethylphenyl	7.50	Isobutyl	9.89
Diethylphenyl	7.75	n-Octyl	9.59
Type RPH_2		2-n-Butoxyethyl	9.85
Butyl	14.03	2-Phenylethyl	10.54
Isobutyl	14.02	Phenyl	13.97
n-Octyl	13.57	2-Cyanoethyl	13.59

[a]Determined in nitromethane, recalculated for water (405); reference Substance Diphenylguanidine.

TABLE II
ACIDITIES OF LEWIS ACIDS (406)[a]

$AlBr_3$	PCl_5
$AlCl_3$	PCl_3
$FeCl_3$	HCl
H_2SO_4 (fuming)	$AsCl_3$
H_2SO_4 (96%)	$ZnCl_2$
$HClO_4$ (70%)	$CdCl_2$
$SnCl_4$	$AuCl_3$
$SbCl_5$	$HgCl_2$
$BiCl_3$	$AgNO_3$

[a]The compounds are arranged in order of decreasing acidity.

TABLE III
BASICITIES OF VERY WEAKLY BASIC COLOR INDICATORS (407)[a]

	pK_B
p-Aminoazobenzene	11.20
Phenylazodiphenylamine	12.48
p-Chloro-o-nitroaniline	14.85
2,4-Dinitroaniline	18.38
Benzalacetophenone	19.61
Anthraquinone	22.15

[a]Calculated from the corresponding pK_A values to permit direct comparison with other bases.

TABLE IV

STABILITIES OF QUATERNARY AMMONIUM BASES (182)[a]

Quaternary ammonium hydroxide	Decomposition half-life (days)	
	At 35°C	At 50°C
Tetramethyl	–	26
Tetraethyl	3	0.2
Tetrapropyl	–	2.5
Tetrabutyl	123	–
Tetrapentyl	–	6.2
Tetrahexyl	–	6.1
Tetraheptyl	154	–
Hexadecyltrimethyl	(200)	–
Ethylhexadecyldimethyl	14	–
Phenyltrimethyl	< 5	–
Methyltributyl	(400)	(35)
Hexadecyldimethylbenzyl	8.5	0.7

[a] Approximately 0.1 N solutions in isopropanol.

TABLE V

DISSOCIATION CONSTANTS IN GLACIAL ACETIC ACID (AT 25°C) (113)

	pK		pK
Perchloric acid	4.87	Sodium acetate	6.68
Sulfuric acid	7.24	Lithium acetate	6.79
p-Toluenesulfonic acid	8.44	2,5-Dichloroaniline	9.48
Hydrochloric acid	8.55	Urea	10.24
Tribenzylamine	5.40	Water	12.53
Pyridine	6.10	Sodium perchlorate	5.48
Potassium acetate	6.15	Potassium chloride	6.88
Dimethylaminoazobenzene	6.32	Urea hydrochloride	6.96
Ammonia	6.40	Lithium chloride	7.08

TABLE VI
DIELECTRIC CONSTANTS, ϵ,[a] AND AUTOPROTOLYSIS CONSTANTS,
pK_{auto}, OF SOLVENTS (AT 20°C UNLESS OTHERWISE STATED)

TABLE VI,1. AMPHIPROTIC SOLVENTS, NEUTRAL

	ϵ	pK_{auto}
Water	80.4	14.00
Methanol	33.6	16.70
Ethanol	25.1	19.10
n-Propanol	20.8	
Isopropanol	19.0	
n-Butanol	17.1 (25°C)	
2-Methyl-2-propanol (*tert*-butanol)	10.9 (30°C)	
Benzyl alcohol	13.0	
Ethylene glycol	38.7	
Cyclohexanol	16.8 (25°C)	

TABLE VI,2. AMPHIPROTIC SOLVENTS, ACIDIC

	ϵ	pK_{auto}
Glacial acetic acid	6.15	14.45
Formic acid	58.5 (25°C)	6.20
Trifluoroacetic acid	8.22	
Sulfuric acid	~ 110.00	
Phenol	9.7 (48°C)	

TABLE VI,3. AMPHIPROTIC SOLVENTS, BASIC

	ϵ
Ammonia	22.0 (−33°C)
Butylamine	5.3 (25°C)
Ethylenediamine	12.9 (25°C)
Formamide	~ 110
Benzylamine	4.6
Piperidine	5.8

TABLE VI,4. Aprotic Solvents, Neutral

	ϵ		ϵ
Ketones:		*Ethers:*	
Acetone	21.2	Diethyl ether	4.2 (25°C)
Methyl ethyl ketone	18.5 (25°C)	Di-*n*-propyl ether	3.4 (25°C)
Methyl isobutyl ketone	13.1 (25°C)	Dimethoxyethane	3.5
Cyclohexanone	16.0	Tetrahydrofuran	8.2
Hydrocarbons and chlorinated hydrocarbons:		1,4-Dioxane	2.2 (25°C)
Benzene	2.3	Anisole	4.3 (25°C)
Toluene	2.4	*Other compounds:*	
Chlorobenzene	5.6 (25°C)	Nitrobenzene	35.7
Chloroform	4.7 (25°C)	Benzonitrile	25.6
Carbon tetrachloride	2.2	Acetonitrile	36.0
Cyclohexane	2.0	Ethyl acetate	6.0
n-Hexane	1.9	Acetic anhydride	20.7
1,2-Dichloroethane	10.2 (25°C)		

TABLE VI,5. Aprotic Solvents, Acidic

	ϵ
Nitromethane	35.9 (25°C)
Nitroethane	29.5

TABLE VI,6. Aprotic Solvents, Basic

	ϵ
Pyridine	13.5
Dimethylformamide	27.0 (25°C)

TABLE VII
DISSOCIATION CONSTANTS OF TETRAISOAMYLAMMONIUM
NITRATE IN WATER/DIOXANE MIXTURES (408)

Dielectric constant of the mixture	pK
38.0	0.60
11.9	3.08
8.50	4.00
5.82	5.78
4.42	7.53
3.48	9.6
2.90	12.0
2.56	14.0

REFERENCES

1. J. N. Brönsted, *Rec. Trav. Chim.* **42**, 718 (1923); *J. Phys. Chem.* **30**, 777 (1926); *Chem. Rev.* **5**, 231 (1928); *Ber. Deut. Chem. Ges.* **61**, 2049 (1928).
2. G. N. Lewis, "Valence and the Structure of Atoms and Molecules." Chem. Catalog Co., New York, 1923.
3. A. Hantzsch, *Z. Physik. Chem.* **A134**, 406 (1928).
4. L. P. Hammett, *Chem. Rev.* **16**, 67 (1935).
5. F. A. Long and M. A. Paul, *Chem Rev.* **57**, 935 (1957).
6. F. E. Critchfield and J. B. Johnson, *Anal. Chem.* **30**, 1247 (1958).
7. C. A. Streuli, *Anal. Chem.* **32**, 407 (1960).
8. R. R. Miron and D. M. Hercules, *Anal. Chem.* **33**, 1770 (1961).
9. C. A. Streuli and R. R. Miron, *Anal. Chem.* **30**, 1978 (1958).
10. M. M. Davis and H. B. Hetzer, *J. Res. Natl. Bur. Std.* **60**, 569 (1958).
11. H. K. Hall, *J. Phys. Chem.* **60**, 63 (1956).
12. C. A. Streuli, *Anal. Chem.* **30**, 997 (1958).
13. C. A. Streuli, *Anal. Chem.* **31**, 1652 (1959).
14. J. P. Wolff, *Anal. Chim. Acta* **1**, 90 (1947).
14a. G. A. Harlow and D. B. Bruss, *Anal. Chem.* **30**, 69 (1958).
15. H. B. van der Heijde, *Anal. Chim. Acta* **16**, 392 (1957).
16. G. A. Harlow and D. B. Bruss, *Anal. Chem.* **30**, 1833 (1958).
17. A. A. Maryott, *J. Res. Natl. Bur. Std.* **38**, 527 (1947).
18. S. Kaufmann and C. R. Singleberry, *J. Phys. Chem.* **56**, 604 (1952).
19. G. M. Barrow, *J. Am. Chem. Soc.* **78**, 5802 (1956).
20. D. B. Bruss and G. A. Harlow, *Anal. Chem.* **30**, 1836 (1958).
21. H. K. Hall, *J. Phys. Chem.* **60**, 63 (1956).
22. J. S. Fritz and S. S. Yamamura, *Anal. Chem.* **29**, 1079 (1957).
23. C. A. Streuli, *Anal. Chem.* **31**, 1652 (1959).
24. R. R. Miron and D. M. Hercules, *Anal. Chem.* **33**, 1770 (1961).
25. R. H. Cundiff and P. C. Markunas, *Anal. Chem.* **28**, 792 (1956).
26. M. L. Moss, J. H. Elliott and R. T. Hall, *Anal. Chem.* **20**, 784 (1948)
27. I. M. Kolthoff and S. Bruckenstein, *J. Am. Chem. Soc.* **78**, 1 (1956).
28. S. Bruckenstein and I. M. Kolthoff, *J. Am. Chem. Soc.* **78**, 10 (1956).
29. I. M. Kolthoff and P. J. Elving, "Treatise on Analytical Chemistry," p. 283 ff. Wiley (Interscience), New York, 1959.
30. S. Bruckenstein and I. M. Kolthoff, *J. Am. Chem. Soc.* **78**, 10 (1956).
31. S. Bruckenstein and I. M. Kolthoff, *J. Am. Chem. Soc.* **78**, 2974 (1956).
32. I. M. Kolthoff and P. J. Elving, "Treatise on Analytical Chemistry," p. 506. Wiley (Interscience), New York, 1959.
33. H. B. van der Heijde and E. A. M. F. Dahmen, *Anal. Chim. Acta* **16**, 378 (1957).

34. F. Hahn, "p_H und potentiometrische Titrierungen." Akad. Verlagsges., Frankfurt a. M. (in preparation) 1964.

35. J. E. Ricci, "Hydrogen Ion Concentration." Princeton Univ. Press, Princeton, New Jersey, 1952.

36. C. F. Tubbs, *Anal. Chem.* **26,** 1670 (1954).

37. F. L. Hahn and G. Weiler, *Z. Anal. Chem.* **69,** 417 (1926).

38. C. Liteanu and D. Cörmös, *Talanta* **7,** 18 (1960).

39. F. L. Hahn, *Mikrochim. Acta* p. 395 (1958).

40. F. L. Hahn, *Z. Anal. Chem.* **183,** 275 (1961).

41. G. Gran, *Analyst* **77,** 661 (1952).

42. M. R. Joseph, *Science* **129,** 1493 (1959).

43. J. M. H. Fortuin, *Anal. Chim. Acta* **24,** 175 (1961).

44. R. H. Müller, *Ind. Eng. Chem., Anal. Ed.* **13,** 724 (1941).

45. G. A. Harlow and D. B. Bruss, *Anal. Chem.* **30,** 1833 (1958).

46. Houben/Weyl, "Physikalische Forschungsmethoden," Vol. 3/2, p. 190. Thieme, Stuttgart, 1955.

47. G. Jander and O. Pfundt, "Die Konduktometrische Massanalyse." Enke, Stuttgart, 1945.

48. W. Böttger, Physikalische Methoden der analytischen Chemie, Akad. Verlagsges., Leipzig, 1949.

49. H. T. S. Britton, "Conductometric Analysis." Chapman & Hall, London, 1934.

50. N. van Meurs and E. A. M. F. Dahmen, *J. Electroanal. Chem.* **1,** 458 (1959–1960).

51. N. van Meurs and E. A. M. F. Dahmen, *Anal. Chim. Acta* **21,** 10 and 193 (1959).

52. E. Bonitz, *Chem. Ber.* **88,** 742 (1955).

53. E. Bonitz and W. Huber, *Z. Anal. Chem.* **186,** 206 (1962).

54. E. Grunwald, *Anal. Chem.* **28,** 1112 (1956).

55. I. M. Kolthoff, *Anal. Chem.* **26,** 1685 (1954).

56. W. Büchler, *Z. Analyt. Chem.* **186,** 154 (1962).

57. K. Cruse, *Dechema Monograph.* **31,** 99 (1958).

58. J. Jordan and T. G. Alleman, *Anal. Chem.* **29,** 9 (1957).

59. R. Belcher, J. Berger, and T. S. West, *J. Chem. Soc.* p. 2877 (1959).

60. M. Gutterson and T. S. Ma, *Mikrochim. Acta,* p. 1 (1960).

61. C. W. Pifer and E. G. Wollish, *Anal. Chem.* **24,** 300 (1952).

62. J. B. Headrige, "Photometric Titrations." Macmillan (Pergamon), New York, 1961.

63. T. Higuchi, C. R. Rehm, and C. Barnstein, *Anal. Chem.* **28,** 1506 (1956).

64. C. R. Rehm and T. Higuchi, *Anal. Chem.* **29,** 367 (1957).

65. K. A. Connors and T. Higuchi, *Anal. Chim. Acta* **25,** 509 (1961).

66. K. A. Connors and T. Higuchi, *Anal. Chem.* **32,** 93 (1960).

67. T. Higuchi, C. Barnstein, H. Ghassemi, and W. E. Perez, *Anal. Chem.* **34,** 400 (1962).

68. R. F. Goddu and D. N. Hume, *Anal. Chem.* **26,** 1740 (1954).

69. R. F. Goddu and D. N. Hume, *Anal. Chem.* **26,** 1679 (1954).

70. L. E. I. Hummelstedt and D. N. Hume, *Anal. Chem.* **32,** 1793 (1960).

71. C. A. Reynolds, F. H. Walker, and E. Cochran, *Anal. Chem.* **32,** 983 (1960).

72. A. Schulze, *Z. Anal. Chem.* **21,** 167 (1882).

73. K. F. Lauer and Y. Le Duigon, *Z. Anal. Chem.* **184,** 4 (1961).

74. F. L. Hahn, *Anal. Chim. Acta* **9,** 400 (1953).

75. J. Minczewski, *Chem. Anal. (Warsaw)* **3,** 453 (1961).

76. H. Palevsky, R. K. Swank, and R. Grenchik, *Rev. Sci. Instr.* **18,** 298 (1947).
77. P. W. Mullen and A. Anton, *Anal. Chem.* **32,** 103 (1960).
78. H. V. Malmstadt and E. R. Fett, *Anal. Chem.* **26,** 1348 (1954).
79. Y. Maekawa, *Pharm. Bull. (Tokyo)* **4,** 321, 325, and 328 (1956).
80. H. V. Malmstadt and E. R. Fett, *Anal. Chem.* **27,** 1757 (1955).
81. H. V. Malmstadt and C. B. Roberts, *Anal. Chem.* **28,** 1884 (1956).
82. H. V. Malmstadt and D. A. Vassallo, *Anal. Chem.* **31,** 863 (1959).
83. H. V. Malmstadt and D. A. Vassallo, *Anal. Chem.* **31,** 206 (1959).
84. H. V. Malmstadt and D. A. Vassallo, *Anal. Chim. Acta* **16,** 455 (1957).
85. H. V. Malmstadt and C. B. Roberts, *Anal. Chem.* **28,** 1408 (1956).
86. G. Halfter, W. Kuttler, and G. Köhler, *Chem. Ingr. Tech.* **31,** 734 (1959).
87. J. S. Fritz and N. M. Lisicki, *Anal. Chem.* **23,** 589 (1951).
88. W. Raehs, Dissertation, Aachen, 1961.
89. G. A. Harlow, *Anal. Chem.* **34,** 148 (1962).
90. L. Michaelis and M. Mizutani, *Biochem. Z.* **147,** 7 (1924).
91. S. Kilpi, *Z. Physik. Chem.* **A177,** 116 (1936).
92. S. Kilpi and M. Puranen, *Z. Physik. Chem.* **A187,** 276 (1940).
93. V. A. Izgarnischew and S. A. Pletenew, *Z. Elektrochem.* **36,** 457 (1930).
94. H. Argenstein, *Roczniki Chem.* **30,** 855 (1956).
95. O. Tomicek and P. Vidner, *Chem. Listy* **47,** 521 (1953).
96. L. P. Hammett and N. Dietz, *J. Am. Chem. Soc.* **52,** 4795 (1930).
97. B. O. Hestan and N. F. Hall, *J. Am. Chem. Soc.* **55,** 4729 (1953).
98. A. Kirrmann and N. Danne-Dubois, *Compt. Rend.* **236,** 1361 (1953).
99. R. Schaal, *J. Chim. Phys.* **52,** 719 (1955).
100. A. M. Shkodin and N. A. Ismailov, *Zh. Obshch. Khim.* **20,** 38 (1950).
101. L. P. Hammett and N. Dietz, *J. Am. Chem. Soc.* **52,** 4795 (1930).
102. G. Gran and B. Althin, *Acta Chem. Scand.* **4,** 967 (1950).
103. G. A. Harlow, C. N. Noble, and E. A. O. Garrard, *Anal. Chem.* **28,** 787 (1956).
104. J. E. de Vries, S. Schiff, and E. S. C. Gantz, *Anal. Chem.* **27,** 1814 (1955).
105. C. J. Lintner, R. H. Schleif, and T. Higuchi, *Anal. Chem.* **22,** 534 (1950).
106. A. R. Tourky, I. M. Issa, and S. A. Awad, *Chim. Anal.* **37,** 367 (1955).
107. M. L. Moss, J. H. Elliott, and R. T. Hall, *Anal. Chem.* **20,** 784 (1948).
108. E. Oirasoro, *Rev. Fac. Ing. Quim. Univ. Nacl. Litoral, Sante Fe, Arg.* **20,** 83 (1951).
109. K. Sandved and H. Harang, *Kgl. Norske Videnskab. Selskabs Forh.* **12,** 41 (1939).
110. O. A. Ohlweiler and J. O. Meditsch, *Eng. Quim. (Rio de Janeiro)* **6,** 1 (1954).
111. L. Lykken and F. D. Tuemmler, *Ind. Eng. Chem., Anal. Ed.* **14,** 67 (1942).
112. O. Tomicek, *Sb. Celostatni Pracovni Konf. Anal. Chemiku, 1st Prague, 1952,* p. 246 (1953).
113. S. Bruckenstein and I. M. Kolthoff, *J. Am. Chem. Soc.* **78,** 2974 (1956).
114. E. Scarano and A. Ceglie, *Anal. Chim. Acta* **12,** 292 (1955).
115. M. W. Tamele and L. B. Ryland, *Ind. Eng. Chem. Anal. Ed.* **8,** 16 (1936).
116. M. Farina, M. Donati, and M. Ragazzini, *Ann. Chim. (Rome)* **48,** 501 (1958).
117a. Houben/Weyl, "Physikalische Forschungsmethoden," Vol. 3/2, p. 92. Thieme, Stuttgart.
117b. L. W. Marple and J. S. Fritz, *Anal. Chem.* **34,** 796 (1962).
118a. B. Gutbezahl and E. Grunwald, *J. Am. Chem. Soc.* **75,** 565 (1953).
118b. D. C. Wimer, *Anal. Chem.* **30,** 77 (1958).

119. J. S. Fritz, *Anal. Chem.* **22,** 1028 (1950).

120. R. A. Glenn, *Anal. Chem.* **25,** 1916 (1953).

121. C. A. Streuli, *Anal. Chem.* **30,** 997 (1958).

122. H. V. Malmstadt and E. R. Fett, *Anal. Chem.* **27,** 1757 (1955).

123. H. V. Malmstadt and D. A. Vassallo, *Anal. Chem.* **31,** 206 (1959).

124. A. R. Tourky, I. M. Issa, and S. A. Awad, *Chim. Anal.* **37,** 367 (1955).

125. G. A. Harlow and D. B. Bruss, *Anal. Chem.* **30,** 1833 (1958).

126. J. B. Conant and N. F. Hall, *J. Am. Chem. Soc.* **49,** 3047 (1927).

127. J. B. Conant and N. F. Hall, *J. Am. Chem. Soc.* **49,** 3062 (1927).

128. J. B. Conant and N. F. Hall, *J. Am. Chem. Soc.* **52,** 4436 (1930).

129. N. F. Hall, *J. Am. Chem. Soc.* **52,** 5115 (1930).

130. N. F. Hall and J. B. Conant, *J. Am. Chem. Soc.* **50,** 2367 (1928).

131. W. C. Eichelberger and V. K. La Mer, *J. Am. Chem. Soc.* **55,** 3633 (1933).

132. S. Bruckenstein, *Anal. Chem.* **31,** 1757 (1959).

133. R. Belcher, J. Berger, and T. S. West, *J. Chem. Soc.* p. 2882 (1959).

134. C. W. Pifer and E. G. Wollish, *Anal. Chem.* **24,** 300 (1952).

135. M. Gutterson and T. S. Ma, *Mikrochim. Acta* p. 1 (1960).

136. A. M. Shkodin and N. A. Izmailov, *Zh. Obshch. Khim.* **20,** 38 (1950).

137. A. M. Shkodin, N. A. Izmailov, and N. P. Dzyuba, *Zh. Analit. Khim.* **6,** 273 (1951).

138. S. G. Terjesen and K. Sandved, *Kgl. Norske Videnskab. Selskabs Skrifter* No. 7 (1938); *Chem. Abstr.* **33,** 4495 (1939).

139. L. G. Chatten, *J. Pharm. Pharmacol.* **7,** 586 (1955).

140. J. E. de Vries, S. Schiff, and E. S. C. Gantz, *Anal. Chem.* **27,** 1814 (1955).

141. M. L. Moss, J. H. Elliott, and R. T. Hall, *Anal. Chem.* **20,** 784 (1948).

142. M. Katz and R. A. Glenn, *Anal. Chem.* **24,** 1157 (1952).

143. J. Hine and M. Hine, *J. Am. Chem. Soc.* **74,** 5266 (1952).

144. J. S. Fritz and L. W. Marple, *Anal. Chem.* **34,** 921 (1962).

145. L. W. Marple and J. S. Fritz, *Anal. Chem.* **35,** 1305 (1963).

146. S. R. Palit, *Ind. Eng. Chem., Anal. Ed.* **18,** 246 (1946).

147. J. E. Ruch, J. B. Johnson, and F. E. Critchfield, *Anal. Chem.* **33,** 1566 (1961).

148. J. E. Ruch and F. E. Critchfield, *Anal. Chem.* **33,** 1569 (1961).

149. J. S. Fritz and M. O. Fulda, *Anal. Chem.* **25,** 1837 (1953).

150. C. A. Streuli, *Anal. Chem.* **31,** 1652 (1959).

151. W. Huber, *Z. Anal. Chem.* **181,** 158 (1961).

152. Unpublished results. 1959.

153. R. H. Cundiff and P. C. Markunas, *Anal. Chem.* **28,** 792 (1956).

154. R. H. Cundiff and P. C. Markunas, *Anal. Chem.* **30,** 1447 (1958).

155. W. Huber, unpublished (1960).

156. M. M. Caso and M. Cefola, *Anal. Chim. Acta* **21,** 205 (1959).

156a. W. Huber, unpublished.

157. A. P. Kreshkov, L. N. Bykova, and N. S. Sheme, *Doklady. Akad. Nauk SSSR* **134,** 96 (1960).

158. N. van Meurs and E. A. M. F. Dahmen, *Anal. Chim. Acta* **21,** 193 (1959).

159. D. B. Bruss and G. E. A. Wyld, *Anal. Chem.* **29,** 232 (1957).

160. J. S. Fritz, *Anal. Chem.* **25,** 407 (1953).

161. J. F. Coetzee, G. P. Cunningham, D. G. Guise, and G. R. Paducanabhan, *Anal. Chem.* **34,** 1139 (1962).

162. J. S. Fritz, *Anal. Chem.* **26,** 1701 (1954).

163. N. van Meurs and E. A. M. F. Dahmen, *Anal. Chim. Acta* **21,** 193 (1959).

164. H. Burton and P. F. G. Prail, *J. Chem. Soc.* pp. 1203 and 2034 (1950); *ibid.* p. 522 (1951).

165. D. C. Wimer, *Anal. Chem.* **30,** 77 (1958).

166. W. Seaman and E. Allen, *Anal. Chem.* **23,** 592 (1951).

167. R. Belcher, J. Berger and T. S. West, *J. Chem. Soc.* p. 2877 (1951).

168. M. Gutterson and T. S. Ma, *Mikrochim. Acta* p. 1 (1960).

169. R. C. Paul, J. Singh and S. S. Sandhu, *J. Indian Chem. Soc.* **36,** 305 (1959).

170. J. S. Fritz, *Anal. Chem.* **25,** 407 (1953).

171. R. H. Cundiff and P. C. Markunas, *Anal. Chem.* **33,** 1028 (1961).

172. G. H. Schenk and J. S. Fritz, *Anal. Chem.* **32,** 987 (1960).

173. C. W. Pifer, E. G. Wollish and M. Schmall, *Anal. Chem.* **25,** 310 (1953).

174. M. M. Caso and M. Cefola, *Anal. Chim. Acta* **21,** 374 (1959).

175. M. M. Davis and H. B. Hetzer, *J. Res. Natl. Bur. Std.* **54,** 309 (1955).

176. E. S. Lane, *Talanta* **8,** 849 (1961).

177. R. C. Paul, S. K. Vasisht, K. C. Malhotra, and S. S. Pahil, *Anal. Chem.* **34,** 820 (1962).

178. R. Belcher, J. Berger, and T. S. West, *J. Chem. Soc.* p. 2882 (1959).

179. R. T. Keen and J. S. Fritz, *Anal. Chem.* **24,** 564 (1952).

180. R. T. Keen, *Anal. Chem.* **23,** 1706 (1951).

181. M. L. Cluett, *Anal. Chem.* **31,** 610 (1959).

182. G. A. Harlow, *Anal. Chem.* **34,** 1487 (1962).

183. H. B. van der Heijde and E. A. M. F. Dahmen, *Anal. Chim. Acta* **16,** 378 (1957).

184. R. H. Cundiff and P. C. Markunas, *Anal. Chem.* **30,** 1450 (1958).

185. G. A. Harlow and G. E. A. Wyld, *Anal. Chem.* **30,** 73 (1958).

185a. Unpublished results (1961).

186. G. A. Harlow, C. N. Noble, and G. E. A. Wyld, *Anal. Chem.* **28,** 787 (1956).

187. J. S. Fritz and S. S. Yamamura, *Anal. Chem.* **29,** 1079 (1957).

188. G. A. Harlow and G. E. A. Wyld, *Anal. Chem.* **34,** 172 (1962).

189. J. S. Fritz and R. T. Keen, *Anal. Chem.* **25,** 179 (1953).

190. N. F. Hall and T. H. Werner, *J. Am. Chem. Soc.* **50,** 2367 (1928).

191. J. B. Conant and T. H. Werner, *J. Am. Chem. Soc.* **52,** 4436 (1930).

192. D. Vorländer, *Ber. Deut. Chem. Ges.* **66,** 1789 (1933); **67,** 145 (1934).

193. R. Dietzel and W. Paul, *Arch. Pharm.* **273,** 507 (1935).

194. R. Dietzel and W. Paul, *Arch. Pharm.* **276,** 408 (1938).

195. G. F. Nadeau and C. E. Branchen, *J. Am. Chem. Soc.* **57,** 1363 (1935).

196. J. S. Fritz, *Anal. Chem.* **22,** 578 (1950).

197. A. F. Gremillion, *Anal. Chem.* **27,** 133 (1955).

198. K. Blumrich and G. Bandel, *Angew. Chem.* **54,** 375 (1941).

199. I. M. Kolthoff and S. Bruckenstein, *J. Am. Chem. Soc.* **78,** 1 (1956).

200. S. Bruckenstein and I. M. Kolthoff, *J. Am. Chem. Soc.* **78,** 10 (1956).

201. P. C. Markunas and J. A. Riddick, *Anal. Chem.* **23,** 337 (1951).

202. J. S. Fritz, "Acid-Base-Titration in Nonaqueous Solvents." Frederick Smith Chemical Co., Columbus, Ohio, 1952.

203. Unpublished results (1960).

204. P. C. Markunas and J. A. Riddick, *Anal. Chem.* **23,** 337 (1951).

205. C. A. Streuli, *Anal. Chem.* **32,** 985 (1960).

206. A. M. Shkodin, N. A. Izmailov, and N. P. Dzyuba, *Zh. Obshch. Khim.* **20**, 1999 (1950).
207. J. E. de Vries, J. H. Elliott, and R. T. Hall, *Anal. Chem.* **20**, 784 (1948).
208. D. C. Wimer, *Anal. Chem.* **34**, 873 (1962).
209. D. C. Wimer, *Anal. Chem.* **30**, 2060 (1958).
210. K. A. Connors and T. Higuchi, *Anal. Chem.* **32**, 93 (1960).
211. L. L. Ciaccio, S. R. Missan, W. H. McMullen, and T. C. Grenfell, *Anal. Chem.* **29**, 1670 (1957).
212. O. Lorenz and C. R. Parks, *Anal. Chem.* **34**, 394 (1962).
213. K. Blumrich and G. Bandel, *Angew. Chem.* **54**, 375 (1941).
214. C. D. Wagner, R. H. Brown, and E. D. Peters, *J. Am. Chem. Soc.* **69**, 2609 (1947).
215. J. Gyenes, *Magyar Kem. Folyoirat* **62**, 26 (1956).
215a. W. Huber, Unpublished results (1959).
216. N. N. Bezinger, G. D. Gal'pern and M. A. Abdurachmanov, *Zh. Analit. Khim.* **16**, 91 (1961).
217. S. Siggia, J. G. Hanna, and I. R. Kervenski, *Anal. Chem.* **22**, 1295 (1950).
218. J. B. Johnson and G. L. Funk, *Anal. Chem.* **28**, 1977 (1956).
219. F. E. Critchfield and J. B. Johnson, *Anal. Chem.* **29**, 957 (1957).
220. W. Huber, *Angew. Chem.* **72**, 865 (1960).
221. F. E. Critchfield and J. B. Johnson, *Anal. Chem.* **28**, 436 (1956).
222. F. E. Critchfield and J. B. Johnson *Anal. Chem.* **29**, 1174 (1957).
223. W. Hawkins, D. M. Smith, and J. Mitchell, *J. Am. Chem. Soc.* **66**, 1662 (1944).
224. S. K. Freeman, *Anal. Chem.* **25**, 1750 (1953).
225. G. D. Gal'pern and N. N. Bezinger, *Zh. Analit. Khim.* **13**, 603 (1958).
226. C. L. Ogg, W. L. Porter, and C. O. Willits, *Ind. Eng. Chem., Anal. Ed.* **17**, 397 (1945).
227. F. E. Critchfield and J. B. Johnson, *Anal. Chem.* **28**, 430 (1956).
228. A. T. Casey and K. Starke, *Anal. Chem.* **31**, 1060 (1959).
229. C. W. Pifer and E. G. Wollish, *Anal. Chem.* **24**, 519 (1952).
230. J. S. Fritz, *Anal. Chem.* **26**, 1701 (1954).
231. S. T. Ross and D. B. Denney, *Anal. Chem.* **32**, 1896 (1960).
232. T. Higuchi and J. Concha, *J. Am. Pharm. Assoc., Sci. Ed.* **40**, 173 (1951).
233. T. Higuchi and J. Concha, *Science* **113**, 210 (1951).
234. G. F. Nadeau and C. E. Branchen, *J. Am. Chem. Soc.* **57**, 1363 (1935).
235. S. Mizukami and E. Hirai, *Japan Analyst* **79**, 457 (1959).
236. G. Goldstein, O. Menis, and D. L. Manning, *Anal. Chem.* **33**, 266 (1961).
237. W. Huber, *Z. Anal. Chem.* **197**, 236 (1963).
238. A. J. Durbetaki, *Anal. Chem.* **28**, 2000 (1956).
239. K. Blumrich and G. Bandel, *Angew. Chem.* **54**, 375 (1941).
240. A. J. Durbetaki, *Anal. Chem.* **30**, 2024 (1958).
241. O. Folin and A. H. Wentworth, *J. Biol. Chem.* **7**, 421 (1909–1910).
242. O. Folin and F. F. Flanders, *J. Am. Chem. Soc.* **34**, 774 (1912).
243. M. L. Moss, J. H. Elliott, and R. T. Hall, *Anal. Chem.* **20**, 784 (1948).
244. J. S. Fritz, *Anal. Chem.* **24**, 674 (1952).
245. J. S. Fritz and R. T. Keen, *Anal. Chem.* **25**, 179 (1953).
246. V. Z. Deal and G. E. A. Wyld, *Anal. Chem.* **27**, 47 (1955).
247. R. H. Cundiff and P. C. Markunas, *Anal. Chem.* **28**, 792 (1956).
248. A. H. Corwin and R. C. Ellingson, *J. Am. Chem. Soc.* **64**, 2098 (1942).

249. T. Higuchi, C. J. Lintner, and R. H. Schleif, *Science* **111**, 63 (1950).
250. T. Higuchi and D. A. Zuck, *J. Am. Chem. Soc.* **73**, 2676 (1951).
251. T. Higuchi, J. Concha, and R. Kuramoto, *Anal. Chem.* **24**, 685 (1952).
252. J. S. Fritz and N. M. Lisicki, *Anal. Chem.* **23**, 589 (1951).
253. M. M. Caso and M. Cefola, *Anal. Chim. Acta* **21**, 205 (1959).
254. J. S. Fritz, *Anal. Chem.* **24**, 306 (1952).
255. C. J. Lintner, R. H. Schleif, and T. Higuchi, *Anal. Chem.* **22**, 534 (1950).
256. R. H. Cundiff and P. C. Markunas, *Anal. Chem.* **30**, 1447 (1958).
257. M. G. Yakubik, L. W. Safranski, and J. Mitchell, *Anal. Chem.* **30**, 1741 (1958).
258. W. Pfab, personal communication, Ludwigshafen/Rhine (1959).
259. G. A. Harlow and G. E. A. Wyld, *Anal. Chem.* **30**, 69 (1958).
260. M. L. Dondon, *J. Chem. Phys.* **54**, 290 304 (1957).
261. N. Bjerrum, *Z. Physik. Chem.* **106**, 219 (1923).
262. C. A. Streuli, *Anal. Chem.* **32**, 407 (1960).
263. H. Brockmann and E. Meyer, *Chem. Ber.* **86**, 1514 (1953).
264. R. P. Mitra and S. K. Chatterji, *J. Sci. Ind. Res. (India)* **20B**, 310 (1961).
265. V. Z. Deal and G. E. A. Wyld, *Anal. Chem.* **27**, 47 (1955).
266. F. E. Critchfield and J. B. Johnson, *Anal. Chem.* **26**, 1803 (1954).
267. M. N. Das and D. Mukherjee, *Anal. Chem.* **31**, 233 (1959).
268. W. Stuck, *Z. Anal. Chem.* **177**, 338 (1960).
268a. W. Huber, Unpublished material (1960).
269. E. E. Underwood and A. L. Underwood, *Talanta* **3**, 249 (1960).
270. R. H. Cundiff and P. C. Markunas, *Anal. Chim. Acta* **21**, 68 (1959).
271. M. L. Cluett, *Anal Chem.* **34**, 1491 (1962).
272. H. E. Zaugg and F. C. Garven, *Anal. Chem.* **30**, 1444 (1958).
273. R. G. Pearson, *J. Am. Chem. Soc.* **71**, 2212 (1949).
274. J. S. Fritz and R. T. Keen, *Anal. Chem.* **24**, 308 (1952).
275. O. Tomicek, *Collection Czech. Chem. Commun.* **13**, 116 (1948).
276. A. J. Sensabaugh, R. H. Cundiff, and P. C. Markunas, *Anal. Chem.* **30**, 1445 (1958).
277. W. Schöniger and H. Lieb, *Mikrochemie Ver. Mikrochim. Acta* **38**, 165 (1951).
278. W. Schöniger, H. Lieb, and K. Gassner, *Mikrochim. Acta* p. 434 (1953).
279. F. Pregl and H. Roth, "Quantitative organische Mikroanalyse," 7th ed. Springer, Vienna, 1958.
280. R. H. Cundiff and P. C. Markunas, *Anal. Chem.* **33**, 1028 (1961).
281. W. T. Robinson, R. H. Cundiff, A. J. Sensabaugh, and P. C. Markunas, *Talanta* **3**, 307 (1960).
282. W. T. Robinson, R. H. Cundiff, and P. C. Markunas, *Anal. Chem.* **33**, 1030 (1961).
283. R. A. Glenn and J. T. Peake, *Anal. Chem.* **27**, 205 (1955).
284. B. Smith and Å. Haglund, *Acta Chem. Scand.* **14**, 1349 (1960).
285. J. S. Fritz, A. J. Moye, and M. J. Richard, *Anal. Chem.* **29**, 1685 (1957).
286. J. Meisenheimer, *Ann. Chem.* **323**, 219 (1902).
287. H. Brockmann and E. Meyer, *Chem. Ber.* **87**, 81 (1954).
288. G. Favini and I. R. Bellobona, *Ann. Chim. (Rome)* **50**, 825 (1960).
289. B. Smith and Å. Haglund, *Acta Chem. Scand.* **15**, 675 (1961).
290. R. D. Sarson, *Anal. Chem.* **30**, 932 (1958).
291. A. J. Everett and G. J. Minkoff, *Trans. Faraday Soc.* **49**, 410 (1953).
292. I. M. Kolthoff and A. J. Medalia, *J. Am. Chem. Soc.* **71**, 3789 (1949).

293. A. J. Martin, *Anal. Chem.* **29,** 79 (1957).

294. L. Barnes and L. J. Molinini, *Anal. Chem.* **27,** 1025 (1955).

295. L. Barnes, *Anal. Chem.* **31,** 405 (1959).

296. M. Gutterson and T. S. Ma, *Microchem. J.* **5,** 601 (1961).

297. W. Deckert, *Z. Anal. Chem.* **176,** 163 (1960).

298. L. Blom and L. Edelhausen, *Anal. Chim. Acta* **13,** 120 (1955).

299. A. Patchornik and J. Shakifin, *Anal. Chem.* **33,** 1887 (1961).

300. L. Blom, L. Edelhagen, and T. Smeets, *Z. Anal. Chem.* **189,** 91 (1962).

300a. W. Huber, Unpublished material (1959).

301. F. Kraus, personal communication, Ludwigshafen, Rhine, 1963.

302. H. Brockmann and E. Meyer, *Chem. Ber.* **86,** 1514 (1953).

303. R. Belcher, J. Berger, and T. S. West, *J. Chem. Soc.* p. 2877 (1959).

304. S. J. Clark, "Quantitative Methods of Organic Microanalysis." Butterworth, London and Washington, D.C., 1956.

305. R. Belcher, L. Serrano-Berges, and T. S. West, *J. Chem. Soc.* p. 3830 (1960).

306. R. T. Keen and J. S. Fritz, *Anal. Chem.* **24,** 564 (1952).

307. M. Gutterson and T. S. Ma, *Mikrochim. Acta* p. 1 (1960).

308. G. Jander, "Die Chemie in wasserähnlichen Lösungsmitteln." Springer, Berlin, 1949.

309. C. Bertoglio-Riolo and T. Soldi, *Ann. Chim. (Rome)* **50,** 1540 (1960).

310. R. C. Paul, J. Singh, and S. S. Sandhu, *Anal. Chem.* **31,** 1495 (1959).

311. F. Oehme, *J. Electroanal. Chem.* **4,** 129 (1962).

312. J. Jordan and T. G. Alleman, *Anal. Chem.* **29,** 9 (1957).

313. H. W. Linde, L. B. Rogers, and D. N. Hume, *Anal. Chem.* **25,** 404 (1953).

314. E. G. Hoffmann and E. Tornau, *Z. Anal. Chem.* **186,** 231 (1962).

315. M. C. Henry, J. F. Hagel, and W. M. McNabb, *Anal. Chim. Acta* **15,** 187 (1956).

316. M. C. Henry, W. M. McNabb, and J. F. Hagel, *Anal. Chim. Acta* **15,** 283 (1956).

317. C. Bertoglio-Riolo, T. Soldi, and C. Oechipinti, *Ann. Chim. (Rome)* **51,** 1178 (1961).

318. G. H. Schenk and M. Ozolins, *Anal. Chem.* **33,** 1562 (1961).

319. E. B. Garber, L. E. D. Pease, and W. F. Luder, *Anal. Chem.* **25,** 581 (1953).

320. A. P. Kreshkov, O. A. Drosdov, and J. G. Vlasova, *Hochschulnachr., Chem. Chem. Technol.* [Izv. Vyssh. Ucheb. Zavedenii, Khim. i Khim. Tekhnol.] **3,** 85 (1960); *Chem. Abstr.* p. 13669 (1961).

321. R. O. Clark, E. V. Ballon, and R. T. Bart, *Anal. Chim. Acta* **23,** 189 (1960).

322. E. Bonitz, *Chem. Ber.* **88,** 742 (1955).

323. E. Bonitz and W. Huber, *Z. Anal. Chem.* **186,** 206 (1962).

324. T. Higuchi and C. R. Rehm, *Anal. Chem.* **27,** 408 (1955).

325. N. van Meurs and E. A. M. F. Dahmen, *Anal. Chim. Acta* **21,** 10 (1959).

326. N. van Meurs and E. A. M. F. Dahmen, *J. Electroanal. Chem.* **1,** 458 (1959).

327. N. van Meurs, *Chem. Weekblad* **54,** 298 (1958).

328. P. J. R. Bryant and A. W. H. Wardrop, *J. Chem. Soc.* p. 895 (1957).

329. D. B. Bruss and G. A. Harlow, *Anal. Chem.* **30,** 1836 (1958).

330. V. K. La Mer and H. C. Downes, *J. Am. Chem. Soc.* **53,** 888 (1931).

331. N. van Meurs and E. A. M. F. Dahmen, *Anal. Chim. Acta* **21,** 193 (1959)

332. W. H. McCurdy and J. Galt, *Anal. Chem.* **30,** 940 (1958).

333. W. Pfab and K. Kiemstedt, unpublished material, BASF Ludwigshafen/Rhine, 1963.

334. W. F. Wagner and W. B. Kauffman, *Anal. Chem.* **25,** 538 (1953).

335. E. S. Lane, *Analyst* **80,** 675 (1955).

336. W. T. Lippincott and A. Timnick. *Anal. Chem.* **28,** 1690 (1956).
337. E. Nebe, *Pharmazie* **14,** 510 (1959).
338. J. A. Dean and E. Cain, *Anal. Chem.* **27,** 212 (1955).
339. K. J. Karrman and G. Johansson, *Mikrochim. Acta* p. 1573 (1956).
340. S. F. Ting, W. S. Jeffery, and E. L. Grove, *Talanta* **3,** 240 (1960).
341. E. L. Grove and W. S. Jeffery, *Talanta* **7,** 56 (1960).
342. G. R. Svoboda, *Anal. Chem.* **33,** 1638 (1961).
343. I. Shain and G. R. Svoboda, *Anal. Chem.* **31,** 1857 (1959).
344. J. E. Dubois and P. C. Lacaze, *Compt. Rend.* **252,** 748 (1961).
345. L. E. I. Hummelstedt and D. N. Hume, *Anal. Chem.* **32,** 576 (1960).
346. C. N. Reilley and B. Schweizer, *Anal. Chem.* **26,** 1124 (1954).
347. C. A. Reynolds, F. H. Walker, and E. Cochran, *Anal. Chem.* **32,** 983 (1960).
348. Yu-Lin G. Liu and C. A. Reynolds, *Anal. Chem.* **34,** 542 (1962).
349. R. W. McKinney and C. A. Reynolds, *Talanta* **1,** 46 (1958).
350. L. E. I. Hummelstedt and D. N. Hume, *Anal. Chem.* **32,** 1793 (1960).
351. W. Ь. Mather and F. C. Anson, *Anal. Chim. Acta* **21,** 468 (1959).
352. C. A. Streuli, *Anal. Chem.* **28,** 130 (1956).
353. R. B. Hanselman and C. A. Streuli, *Anal. Chem.* **28,** 918 (1956).
354. A. S. Meyer and C. M. Boyd, *Anal. Chem.* **31,** 215 (1959).
355. E. Barendrecht and J. G. F. Doornekamp, *Z. Anal. Chem.* **186,** 176 (1962).
356. J. H. McClure, T. M. Roder, and R. H. Kinsey, *Anal. Chem.* **27,** 1599 (1955).
357. S. Siggia and N. A. Floramo, *Anal. Chem.* **25,** 797 (1953).
358. L. M. Litwinenko, D. N. Alexandrowa, and V. G. Napadajlo, *J. Anal. Chem. USSR (English Transl.)* **16,** 226 (1961); ref. in *Z. Anal. Chem.* **186,** 223 (1962).
359. C. P. A. Kappelmeier, "Chemical Analysis of Resin-Based Coating Materials," p. 153. Wiley (Interscience), New York, 1959.
360. D. M. Smith and W. M. D. Bryant, *J. Am. Chem. Soc.* **58,** 2452 (1936).
360a. W. Huber, Unpublished material (1959).
361. Berl/Lunge, "Chemisch-technische Untersuchungsmethoden," 8th ed., Vol. 3, p. 778. Springer, Berlin, 1932.
362. S. Siggia and J. G. Hanna, *Anal. Chem.* **23,** 1717 (1951).
363. J. B. Johnson and G. L. Funk, *Anal. Chem.* **27,** 1464 (1955).
364. A. Patchornik and S. E. Rogozinsky, *Anal. Chem.* **31,** 985 (1959).
365. C. R. Stahl and S. Siggia, *Anal. Chem.* **28,** 1971 (1956).
366. L. J. Lohr, *Anal. Chem.* **32,** 1166 (1960).
367. E. G. Wollish, C. W. Pifer, and M. Schmall, *Anal. Chem.* **26,** 1704 (1954).
368. P. Kemy, J. P. Billon, and F. Bĕgeard, *Ann. Pharm. Franç.* **17,** 284 (1959).
369. C. W. Pifer and E. G. Wollish, *Anal. Chem.* **24,** 300 (1952).
370. S. Wolf, *Naturwissenschaften* **46,** 649 (1959).
371. O. Tomicek, *Collection Czech. Chem. Commun.* **13,** 116 (1948).
372. S. M. Tuthill, O. W. Kolling, and K. H. Roberts, *Anal. Chem.* **32,** 1678 (1960).
373. L. Major and K. M. Papay, *Z. Anal. Chem.* **184,** 222 (1961).
374. J. Sokolowski and S. Kolka, *Chem. Anal. (Warsaw)* **6,** 331 (1961).
375. J. S. Fritz and M. O. Fulda, *Anal. Chem.* **25,** 1837 (1953).
376. L. Levi and C. G. Farmilo, *Anal. Chem.* **25,** 909 (1953).
377. L. Levi, P. M. Oestreicher, and C. G. Farmilo, *Bull. Narcotics, U.N. Dept. Social Affairs* **5,** 15 (1953).

378. M. Schmall, C. W. Pifer, and E. G. Wollish, *Anal. Chem.* **24,** 1446 (1952).
379. M. C. Vincent and M. J. Blake, *J. Am. Pharm. Assoc., Sci. Ed.* **48,** 359 (1959).
380. J. A. Gautier, F. Pellerin, and J. Pineau, *Ann. Pharm. Franc.* **16,** 625 (1958).
381. L. G. Chatten, *J. Am. Pharm. Assoc., Sci. Ed.* **45,** 556 (1956).
382. C. Stainier, C. Lapiere, and S. de Tiege-Robinet, *Ann. Pharm. Franc.* **14,** 384 and 476 (1956).
383. G. Wittmann, *Angew. Chem.* **60,** 330 (1948).
384. C. Deptula, *Chem. Anal. (Warsaw)* **6,** No. 1, 91 (1961).
385. I. Kukin, *Anal. Chem.* **30,** 1114 (1958).
386. V. Z. Deal, F. T. Weiss, and T. W. White, *Anal. Chem.* **25,** 426 (1953).
387. D. B. Bruss and G. E. A. Wyld, *Anal. Chem.* **29,** 232 (1957).
388. J. W. Kimball, R. L. Kramer, and E. E. Reid, *J. Am. Chem. Soc.* **43,** 1199 (1921).
389. S. Siggia and R. Edsberg, *Anal. Chem.* **20,** 938 (1948).
390. R. H. Turk and E. E. Reid, *Ind. Eng. Chem. Anal. Ed.* **5,** 257 (1933).
390a. W. Huber, Unpublished material (1959).
391. D. C. Gregg, P. E. Bouffard, and R. Barton, *Anal. Chem.* **33,** 269 (1961).
392. J. S. Fritz and T. A. Palmer, *Anal. Chem.* **33,** 98 (1961).
393. I. M, Kolthoff and W. E. Harris, *Ind. Eng. Chem. Anal. Ed.* **18,** 161 (1946).
394. M. W. Tamele and L. B. Ryland, *Ind. Eng. Chem. Anal. Ed.* **8,** 16 (1936).
395. J. H. Karchmer, *Anal. Chem.* **30,** 80 (1958).
396. L. Lykken and F. D. Tuemmler, *Ind. Eng. Chem., Anal. Ed.* **14,** 67 (1942).
397. J. H. Karchmer, *Anal. Chem.* **29,** 425 (1957).
398. M. W. Tamele, L. B. Ryland, and R. N. McCay, *Anal. Chem.* **32,** 1007 (1960).
399. H. Schindler, G. W. Ayers, and L. M. Henderson, *Ind. Eng. Chem., Anal. Ed.* **13,** 327 (1941).
400. J. H. Karchmer and M. T. Walker, *Anal. Chem.* **30,** 85 (1958).
401. C. R. Stahl and S. Siggia, *Anal. Chem.* **29,** 154 (1957).
401a. T. E. Earle, *Anal. Chem.* **25,** 769 (1953).
402. A. Albert and E. P. Serjeant, "Ionization Constants of Acids and Bases." Wiley, New York and Meuthen, London, 1962.
403. F. Seel, "Fundamentals of Analytical Chemistry and Chemistry of Aqueous Solutions." Verlag Chemie, Weinheim, 1955.
404. B. E. Conway, "Electrochemical Data." Amsterdam, 1952.
405. C. A. Streuli, *Anal. Chem.* **32,** 985 (1960).
406. D. K. Hawke and J. Steigman, *Anal. Chem.* **26,** 1989 (1954).
407. R. V. Rice, S. Zuffanti, and W. F. Luder, *Anal. Chem.* **24,** 1022 (1952).
408. R. M. Fuoss and C. A. Kraus, *J. Am. Chem. Soc.* **55,** 476 (1933).
409. C. A. Streuli, *Anal. Chem.* **27,** 1827 (1956).
410. S. Wolf and B. Möbus, *Z. Anal. Chem.* **186,** 194 (1962)

AUTHOR INDEX

Numbers in parentheses are reference numbers and indicate that an author's work is referred to although his name is not cited in the text. Numbers in italics show the page on which the complete reference is listed.

A

Abdurachmanov, M. A., 123 (216), *236*
Albert, A., 215 (402), *240*
Alexandrowa, D. N., 197 (358), *239*
Allen, E., 86 (166), 94 (166), 107 (166), *235*
Alleman, T. G., 36 (58), 186 (312), *232, 238*
Althin, B., 62 (102), 67, *233*
Anson, F. C., 195 (351), *239*
Anton, A., 53 (77), *233*
Argenstein, H., 61 (94), *233*
Awad, S. A., 63 (106), 67, *233, 234*
Ayers, G. W., 209 (399), *240*

B

Ballon, E. V., 188 (321), *238*
Bandel, G., 105, 106, 120 (213), 138 (239), *235, 236*
Barendrecht, E., 195 (355), *239*
Barnes, L., 177 (294), 178 (295), *238*
Barnstein, C., 39 (63), 40 (63, 67), *232*
Barrow, G. M., 13 (19), *231*
Bart, R. T., 188 (321), *238*
Barton, R., 207 (391), *240*
Bĕgeard, F., 203 (368), *239*
Belcher, R., 38 (59), 74 (133), 87, 93 (178), 180 (303), 184 (303, 305), 185 *232, 234, 235, 238*
Bellobona, I. R., 174 (288), *237*
Berger, J., 38 (59), 74 (133), 87 (167). 93 (178), 180 (303), 184 (303), *232, 234, 235, 238*

Bertoglio-Riolo, C., 186 (309), 187 (309, 317), *238*
Bezinger, N. W., 123 (216), 125, *236*
Billon, J. P., 203 (368), *239*
Bjerrum, N., 151 (261), *237*
Blake, M. J., 204 (379), *240*
Blom, L., 178 (298), 179, *238*
Blumrich, K., 105, 106, 120 (213), 138 (239), *235, 236*
Böttger, W., 29 (48)
Bonitz, E., 31 (52, 53), 188 (322, 323), *232, 238*
Bouffard, P. E., 207 (391), *240*
Boyd, C. M., 195 (354), *239*
Branchen, L. E., 105 (195), 136, *235, 236*
Britton, H. T. S., 29 (49), *232*
Brockmann, H., 153 (263), 174 (287), 175 (287), 180 (302), 181 (302), *237, 238*
Brönsted, J. N., 4, *231*
Brown, R. H., 120 (214), 123 (214), *236*
Bruckenstein, S., 19, 63 (113), 67, 74, 106, 226 (113), *231, 233, 234, 235*
Bruss, D. B., 13, 14 (20), 29 (45), 71 (125), 83, 188 (329), 205 (387), *231, 232, 234, 238, 240*
Bryant, P. J. R., 188 (328), *238*
Bryant, W. M. D., 198 (360), 199 (360), *239*
Büchler, W., 35, *232*
Burton, H., 85 (164), *235*
Bykova, L. N., 82 (157), *234*

241

SUBJECT INDEX